The British Murder Quiz Book

D. A. Lewis is a Detective Inspector at New Scotland Yard, with over twenty years' service in the police. A member of Mensa, he also has a degree from the Open University and is currently working towards a B.Sc. (Honours) in Psychology. The idea for this book came while he was on holiday looking for a quiz book on murder. Since there wasn't one to be found, he decided to write it himself. He hopes to continue writing on true crime

D. A. Lewis

THE BRITISH MURDER QUIZ BOOK

PAN BOOKS
LONDON, SYDNEY AND AUCKLAND

First published 1994 by Pan Books Ltd

This edition published by Pan Books
an imprint of Pan Macmillan Ltd
Pan Macmillan, 20 New Wharf Road, London N1 9RR
Basingstoke and Oxford
Associated companies throughout the world
www.panmacmillan.com

ISBN 0 330 33374 7

9 8 7 6 5 4 3 2

A CIP catalogue record for this book is available from
the British Library.

Typeset by CentraCet Limited, Cambridge
Printed and bound in Great Britain by
Mackays of Chatham plc, Chatham, Kent

To Barbara (Lars, Erik and Carol) and all those 'great detectives' without whom this book would not have been possible; not forgetting my agent Darley Anderson and my editor, adviser and friend, Ingrid Connell, whose help has been invaluable.

D. A. L.

CONTENTS

PREFACE

As an avid student, over the years, of famous and infamous British murder cases, I felt it was high time that thousands of other similarly devoted readers had a chance to test their knowledge of this sometimes gruesome yet always fascinating subject. Having been unable to find a suitable quiz book, I decided to write one myself!

Within these pages over 250 years of the more sensational side of British social history are condensed into 1,350 questions and answers. Names, places, motives, methods, fears, jealousies and endings all combine to test not only the reader's recall but also his or her depth of understanding.

The format means that anyone from a complete novice to an acknowledged expert can use the book. Whether competing directly against the questions or with friends, whether answering immediately for higher marks, or with the use of Clues to gain lower ones, the possibilities for fun and edification are clear.

INTRODUCTION

Each chapter in this book deals with a particular type of classic British murder cases, from either its methodology, its venue or its judicial disposal, and contains 150 questions. These increase in difficulty as the chapter progresses and each question is rated for the number of points awarded for a correct answer (R1 to R5). At the end of a particular chapter or, indeed, the whole book, your score can be compared with the Self-Rating Chart giving you an idea of how well you have done.

Answering a question correctly will score you the number of points for which that question is rated. If you are having difficulty you may consult the Clues section. Here the true answer will be one of the three listed options. Answering correctly, after consulting the Clues, gains you only half the rated points for that question.

Alternatively you can play the quiz as a game with others. Make up your own rules about question selection, level of difficulty and number of accesses to Clues before you start (use dice for chapter and question numbers if you wish). At the end of a game simply compare scores.

I wish you the best of luck and lots of fun!

PART ONE

QUESTIONS

CHAPTER ONE

THE POISONERS

Question Rating (R1)

1 What was unique, in criminal history, about the arrest of Dr Hawley Harvey Crippen in 1910?

> **2** What was the verdict in the famous 1957 murder trial of Dr John Bodkin Adams, who was accused of poisoning a patient?

3 Of whose murder in 1889 was the notorious Victorian poisoner Florence Maybrick convicted?

> **4** Which metallic poison is generally regarded as that most commonly used by would-be murderers?

5 Which family member was Herbert Rowse Armstrong convicted of murdering in April 1922?

> **6** What was the name of Dr Crippen's mistress, with whom he was arrested?

7 What was poisoner Herbert Rowse Armstrong's profession?

> **8** What was the name of the schoolboy poisoner sent to Broadmoor in 1962 and released in 1971 only to poison again?

9 How was Dr Crippen's mistress disguised on their transatlantic escape bid in 1910?

10 Whom did Ethel Lillie Major poison in 1934?

11 What was the 'stage name' of Dr Hawley Harvey Crippen's wife, Cora?

12 How did poisoner Christiana Edmunds administer the dose which killed a four-year-old boy in 1871?

13 What nationality was Marcus Marymont, charged in 1958 with the murder of his wife and wrongfully having sexual intercourse with another woman?

14 In which region of England did the notorious poisoner Mary Ann Cotton live at the time she committed her crime in 1872?

15 What type of business did the poisoner Dorothea Waddingham, hanged in 1936 for the murder of Ada Baguley, run?

16 Which famous poisoner lived at 39 Hilldrop Crescent, Camden Town, London?

17 What was the nickname of the poisoner Charlotte Bryant, reflecting her country of origin?

18 What first alerted the police to the fact that Ethel Lillie Major's victim may have died in suspicious circumstances in 1934?

19 What was the country of birth of poisoner George Chapman who was hanged in London in April 1903?

20 Of whose murder was Charlotte Bryant convicted in 1936?

21 What was the nationality of poisoner Jean-Pierre Vaquier convicted in 1924?

22 Of which of the 'arts' was Cora Crippen, the wife and victim of Dr Crippen, a poor but enthusiastic devotee?

23 Where was the notorious Victorian poisoner Dr Thomas Neill Cream born?

24 What was the name of the famous Eastbourne doctor, tried at the Old Bailey in 1957 for murder by poisoning?

25 In which county did Jean-Pierre Vaquier both commit his crime and stand trials in 1924?

26 In what capacity was Ethel Le Neve employed by the, subsequently convicted, poisoner Dr Crippen?

27 What was the name of the lady who appeared at the Old Bailey in 1886 charged with murdering her husband with liquid chloroform, in a celebrated Victorian murder trial?

28 Before what sort of court was the poisoner Marcus Marymont tried in 1958?

29 To what specific group of victims did poisoner Dr Thomas Neill Cream dispense his lethal pills in Victorian London?

30 What military rank did the poisoner Herbert Rowse Armstrong hold?

Question Rating (R2)

31 In the trial of Adelaide Bartlett in 1886 for the poisoning of her husband with liquid chloroform, how had the poison been administered?

> **32** According to known figures, approximately what percentage of homicides in Britain are due to poisoning?

33 For what other infamous series of murders was poisoner George Chapman, executed in London in 1903, a suspect?

> **34** Which poison did murderess Charlotte Bryant administer to her victim in 1935?

35 What military rank did Marcus Marymont, convicted of the murder by poisoning of his wife in 1958, hold?

> **36** In which county was Charlotte Bryant living in 1935 when she administered poison to her victim?

37 In what sort of location did poisoner Jean-Pierre Vaquier murder his victim Alfred Jones in 1924?

> **38** By what famous method was it alleged that Florence Maybrick had obtained the arsenic she used to poison her victim?

39 In which town in the 1870s did the notorious poisoner Christiana Edmunds commit her crimes?

> **40** To which institution was the convicted poisoner Graham Young committed in 1962?

41 What was Jean-Pierre Vaquier's motive for the 1924 murder of his host, Alfred Jones?

42 In which county did Ethel Lillie Major live at the time she committed her crimes in 1934?

43 What toxin did Marcus Marymont administer to his wife bringing about her death in 1958?

44 Which members of his family did the poisoner Arthur Devereux, hanged in 1905, murder?

45 What was the peculiar physical feature of the notorious poisoner Dr Thomas Neill Cream, which one of his victims reported?

46 What was Mary Ann Cotton's defence to the charge of murdering her stepson by poisoning in 1872?

47 What was poisoner George Chapman's occupation when arrested in 1902?

48 What did poisoner Frederick Seddon and his trial judge have in common?

49 To what animal did Ethel Lillie Major administer poison, the night before her human victim died, in 1934?

50 When the 1930s murderess Charlotte Bryant first met her farm labourer husband, what was his occupation?

51 What extraordinary claim did the Victorian poisoner Dr Thomas Neill Cream attempt to make, as he fell through the trapdoor of the scaffold in 1892?

52 Whom were John and Janet Armstrong accused of murdering by poison in 1956? (Janet Armstrong was subsequently acquitted.)

53 At her trial in 1958 how many husbands was Mary Elizabeth Wilson alleged to have poisoned?

54 When Dr Crippen and his wife Cora left New York to live in London in the early 1900s in what capacity did he earn a living?

55 What was the occupation of convicted poisoner William Palmer, who was hanged in 1856?

56 What was the verdict in the 1857 Edinburgh trial of Madeleine Smith, accused of the murder by poisoning of her paramour?

57 At his 1957 trial with which poison was it alleged that Dr John Bodkin Adams had disposed of his victim?

58 In which country did the Victorian poisoner Dr Thomas Neill Cream receive a life sentence for murder, prior to his conviction in England?

59 In 1933 whom did killer Samuel Furnace poison?

60 Which poison did Herbert Rowse Armstrong employ on his victim(s) in 1921?

Question Rating (R3)

61 What was the occupation of Frederick Seddon, the poisoner hanged at Pentonville Prison in 1912?

62 Which poison did George Chapman use on his victims in the early 1900s?

63 Ethel Lillie Major, convicted of murder in 1934, passed off her illegitimate daughter as which relative?

64 In 1871 Christiana Edmunds attempted to poison the wife of a local worthy with whom she had fallen in love. What was his occupation?

65 Which poison did Jean-Pierre Vaquier administer to his victim in 1924?

66 What was the occupation of the Victorian poisoner Florence Maybrick's husband, James?

67 What type of poison did Dr Thomas Neill Cream, hanged in 1892, administer to all his victims?

68 Whom did poisoner Richard Brinkley intend to murder in Croydon, Surrey, in 1906?

69 Which poison was Mary Elizabeth Wilson alleged to have administered to all of her victims in 1957?

70 What was the occupation of Kenneth Barlow, sentenced to life imprisonment in 1957 for the murder of his wife by poisoning?

71 What was the basis of Christiana Edmunds' defence to a charge of murder in 1872?

72 What poison did John Armstrong administer to his victim in 1955?

73 What was the place of origin of Madeleine Smith's foreign paramour Pierre Emile L'Angelier, poisoned by arsenic in 1857?

74 What was the name of the ship on which Dr Crippen made his attempted escape from Antwerp to Canada in 1910?

75 Where did the poisoner Graham Young live at the time he committed his original crime in 1962?

76 Which type of sporting event was William Palmer attending, in 1855, which precipitated his murder of John Cook?

77 Where did the compulsive Victorian poisoner Thomas Griffiths Wainewright die, a convict, at the age of fifty-eight?

78 Which poison was found at the post-mortem in 1876 of the wealthy barrister Charles Bravo?

79 For which diseased part of his anatomy was poison victim Edwin Bartlett receiving treatment when he died in 1885?

80 Which poison had Edward William Pritchard administered to his victim(s)?

81 In what medium was the poison Jean-Pierre Vaquier administered to his victim disguised?

82 For whose murders was Edward William Pritchard tried in Edinburgh in 1865?

83 What was Richard Brinkley's motive for administering poison to his victim(s) in 1906?

84 What was the effect of the so-called 'Palmer Act' passed by Parliament in the wake of William Palmer's crime?

85 When the poisoner Charlotte Bryant murdered her husband Frederick in 1935 she had previously taken their lodger Leonard Parsons, as a lover. What was his colourful background?

86 What age was Graham Young when originally sentenced in 1962?

87 Which poison was found in the Victorian murderer William Palmer's victims?

88 At his trial, in 1903, how many people was poisoner George Chapman charged with murdering?

89 What was the profession of George Dyson, Adelaide Bartlett's associate, who purchased chloroform for her in 1885?

> **90** In 1941 where did the Victorian poisoner Florence Maybrick die at the age of seventy-eight?

Question Rating (R4)

91 In 1962, which poison did Graham Young administer to his stepmother with fatal results?

> **92** In which Welsh town in 1921 did the murderer Herbert Rowse Armstrong have his business premises?

93 What was the name of the young bachelor with whom Florence Maybrick had developed a liaison in 1889?

> **94** Which poison did Ethel Lillie Major use to dispose of her victim(s), in 1934?

95 What was unique about the *modus operandi* of poisoner Graham Young?

> **96** In which country did the Victorian poisoner Dr Thomas Neill Cream obtain his medical qualifications?

97 To which prison was poisoner Marcus Marymont sent to serve his life sentence (later reduced to thirty-five years), following his trial in 1958?

> **98** Why is it thought that Dr John Houston, who first examined the body of poison victim Mrs Clements in 1947, took his own life?

99 Which poison did Richard Brinkley make use of in 1906?

100 What, initially, brought Edward William Pritchard under suspicion as a poisoner in 1865?

101 In what medium did Richard Brinkley's victims, in 1906, ingest the poison he had introduced?

102 What household poison did Susan Barber administer to her victim, leading to her 1982 trial at Chelmsford Crown Court?

103 What was the occupation of poisoner William Charles Waite, convicted of the murder of his wife in 1970?

104 For what crime was poisoner Thomas Griffiths Wainewright sentenced to transportation for life in the 1830s?

105 Apart from their crimes what else did poisoners Edward William Pritchard, executed in 1865 and Frederick Henry Seddon, executed in 1912, have in common?

106 What was unique about the poison used by Dr Hawley Harvey Crippen?

107 Although Dr John Bodkin Adams was suspected of poisoning a number of individuals during his thirty-five years as a medical practitioner in Eastbourne, why was no evidence, other than that relating to the specific female with whose murder he was currently charged, allowed at his trial in 1957?

108 Which poison did Arthur Devereux administer to his victims?

109 In what type of firm was Graham Young employed when he poisoned colleagues in 1971?

110 Which unusual poison did Israel Lipski use on his victim Miriam Angel in 1887?

111 Of what offences was Dr John Bodkin Adams convicted in 1957, in a quite separate trial from the one he faced in the same year for murder?

112 What was the occupation of the poisoner John Armstrong, convicted in 1956?

113 Eugene-Marie Chantrelle was convicted in Edinburgh of the 1878 murder of his wife Elizabeth, by poisoning. What was his occupation when he first met her in 1867 and she was fourteen years old?

114 In 1947 a coroner's jury had found that Mrs Amy Clements had been fatally poisoned by her husband Dr Robert Clements. Why was he never brought to trial?

115 In 1953 housekeeper Louisa May Merrifield was convicted of the murder by poisoning of her elderly employer in Blackpool. Which poison did she use?

116 What present was the subsequently convicted poisoner Graham Young given by his father as a reward for passing his eleven-plus examination?

117 At which prison was Ethel Lillie Major hanged in 1934?

118 Shortly after her life sentence for murder began, Susan Barber was briefly allowed out of Holloway Prison in 1983. Why?

119 Which poison did Dorothea Waddingham administer to her victim in 1935?

120 What was the name of the nanny employed by Florence Maybrick who gave incriminating evidence against her at her trial?

Question Rating (R5)

121 Of whose murder was poisoner Susan Barber convicted at Chelmsford Crown Court in 1982?

122 Whose death in December 1906 made it imperative that Richard Brinkley administer poison to his intended victim?

123 In which name did poisoner Jean-Pierre Vaquier sign the poison book at a London chemist?

124 What was poisoner Richard Brinkley's occupation at the time he committed his crime, in 1906?

125 Which famous landmark had been designed by the father of notorious Victorian poisoner Christiana Edmunds?

126 What motive did Ethel le Neve, allegedly, say (in 1930) that Dr Crippen had had for murdering his wife?

127 What is the best estimate of the number of victims the mass murderer May Ann Cotton poisoned before she was hanged in 1873?

128 Which poison did Kenneth Barlow, sentenced to life imprisonment in 1957, use on his victim?

129 What was the occupation of Edward Ernest Black, executed in 1922 for the murder of his wife by arsenic poisoning?

130 Which poison was it alleged that the murderer Eugene-Marie Chantrelle had used on his wife, resulting in his execution in 1878?

131 Of approximately how many victims was the Victorian poisoner William Palmer the possible murderer?

132 For what reasons, in 1859, was the death sentence reprieved and a pardon subsequently granted to Dr Thomas Smethurst who had been found guilty of poisoning with arsenic his bigamous wife, in Richmond?

133 In 1871 what, specifically, did Christiana Edmunds give to her first intended victim in an attempt to poison her?

134 In which county did poisoner Edward Ernest Black murder his wife in 1921?

135 What was the popular name given at the time to the series of illnesses which afflicted the associates of the murderer Graham Young in the early 1970s, and which were eventually found to have been caused by poisoning?

136 In which other European country, to which he had fled prior to his trial, did Victorian poisoner Thomas Griffiths Wainewright murder a man?

137 What did the convicted poisoner Dr Crippen conceal in his clothing hoping to take his own life, while in the death cell in 1910?

138 What was the occupation of the notorious Glaswegian poisoner Edward William Pritchard, tried in Edinburgh in 1865?

139 In which county was the alleged poisoner Adelaide Bartlett born?

140 What was unique in British criminal history about Herbert Rowse Armstrong, the poisoner executed for murder in 1922?

141 What was significant about the execution of Edward William Pritchard, in 1865, in Glasgow?

142 What was Dr Crippen's final request, prior to his 1910 execution, which was subsequently granted?

143 Which relative of the multiple poisoner Arthur Devereux was, because of her strenuous and persistent enquiries, instrumental in bringing him to justice in 1905?

144 Which poison did Frederick Henry Seddon administer to his victim?

145 Whom did the murderess Mary Blandy poison, as the result of a love affair, at her Henley-on-Thames home in 1751?

146 With which poison had Brian Burdett allegedly killed his wife Moira, in their London home in 1956?

147 What was unique in British legal history about one of the murder charges brought against Graham Young in 1972?

148 Following her release from prison in 1904, Florence Maybrick published a book about her experiences. What was its title?

149 What was unique in British criminal history about the Old Bailey poison trial of Adelaide Bartlett in 1886?

150 Where did the trial of the notorious provincial poisoner Christiana Edmunds take place in 1872?

CHAPTER TWO

THE STRANGLERS

Question Rating (R1)

1 When a victim is strangled what is the actual cause of death?

    2 At what subsequently infamous address in the Notting Hill district of London had Timothy John Evans, convicted of murder in 1950, resided at the time of his alleged crime?

3 In which city did the strangler known as 'Bible John' operate in the late 1960s?

    4 What relation were Ian and Allyson Kirk, convicted of the 1985 murder of Miss Ivy Preston in Bradford, Yorkshire?

5 At the time of the 1983 Peter Reyn-Bardt murder trial to whom was it now established that the skull, believed to have possibly been that of the victim Malika Reyn-Bardt, had actually belonged?

    6 Which infamous murderer also occupied the house in Notting Hill, London, where Timothy John Evans was alleged to have strangled his victim?

7 At this trial in 1942 whom was Harry Dobkin convicted of murdering?

8 Dr Buck Ruxton was executed in 1936 for the murder of his wife. Where, in the United Kingdom, had her dismembered body been discovered?

9 In 1928 Chung Yi Miao was tried for a murder in the Lake District. What relation to him was the victim?

10 The identification evidence concerning which item of jewellery played a significant part in the conviction of Herbert John Bennett in 1901?

11 What was the nationality of murderer Chung Yi Miao convicted and executed in 1928?

12 What was notable about the sexual orientation of strangler Sidney Harry Fox, convicted in 1930?

13 In which city in 1959 did the killer Patrick Joseph Byrne first strangle, then mutilate, the body of his female victim?

14 At his trial in June 1984, which sentence was conferred on the convicted murderer Kiernan Kelly, an Irish vagrant, for the second time in a fortnight?

15 By what method did the strangler Sidney Harry Fox attempt to disguise his victim's cause of death in 1929?

16 What was the name of murderer Herbert John Bennett's famous Victorian defence counsel?

17 What was the country of origin of the murderess Styllou Pantopiou Christofi, executed in 1954?

18 When David Greenwood was convicted of murdering Nellie Trew in 1918 what item of clothing, left at the scene, led to his arrest?

19 Which infamous Victorian murderess was known as the 'Reading Baby Farmer'?

20 From which country did the murderer Dr Buck Ruxton, executed in 1936, originally come?

21 Why was the notorious strangler of women in the late 1960s, 'Bible John', so called?

22 In which Commonwealth country was Thomas John Ley, convicted of the murder of John Mudie in the famous 'Chalkpit Murder' of 1946, a one-time Minister of Justice?

23 Which aspect of police investigative techniques was seriously called into question by the Maxwell Confait case in 1972?

24 The body of Chung Yi Miao's victim had been arranged so as to suggest what?

25 At his trial in 1936, how many people was Dr Buck Ruxton convicted of murdering?

26 What did all the victims of the notorious strangler Amelia Elizabeth Dyer have in common?

27 What nationality was Wills Eugene Boshears, tried for the murder of Jean Constable, at the Essex Assizes in 1961?

28 The absence of what in the lungs, at a 1929 post-mortem examination of Sidney Fox's victim, indicated foul play?

29 What had the strangler David Greenwood used to murder his victim Nellie Trew in 1918?

30 What relation was the killer of Miss Lilian Chubb, a middle-aged store employee strangled in 1958 in Broadstairs, Kent, to her victim?

Question Rating (R2)

31 In 1923, how did Susan Newell all too obviously move the body of her victim around Glasgow?

32 What previous offence, for which he had been imprisoned, had the subsequently convicted murderer James Pollard perpetrated on his victim, Zoe Wade, more than two years before her death in 1984?

33 What was the name of the legendary pathologist who carried out the 1929 post-mortem examination on strangler Sidney Harry Fox's victim(s)?

34 By what classic method was the identity of the body of Rachel Dobkin confirmed, after its discovery in July 1942, following her murder by strangulation many months previously?

35 At what type of institution did Patrick Joseph Byrne kill a young woman in 1959?

36 What was the true identity of the murderer known in the late 1960s as 'Bible John'?

37 In which county did the murder of ten-year-old schoolgirl Mona Tinsley, by Frederick Nodder, take place in 1937?

38 What article of clothing had Leslie Stone used to strangle his ex-girlfriend Ruby Keen, in 1937?

39 In which South Coast town did William Sanchez de Pina Hepper strangle eleven-year-old Margaret Spevick in 1954?

40 What was the profession of William Sanchez de Pina Hepper, convicted of the murder of schoolgirl Margaret Spevick in 1954?

41 What verdict was returned at the trial of Wills Eugene Boshears, at the Essex Assizes in 1961, for the murder of Jean Constable?

42 What was the family relationship between the murderess Styllou Pantopiou Christofi and the victim she killed in London in 1954?

43 For whose murder, by strangulation, was Timothy John Evans tried at the Old Bailey in 1950?

44 Which classic clue enabled the police to confirm the *real* identity of Herbert John Bennett's victim 'Mrs Hood' in 1900?

45 What was granted, following the report of an inquiry in 1966, to Timothy John Evans, convicted of murder in 1950?

46 For which famous organization had the strangler William Sanchez de Pina Hepper once worked as a translator?

47 What pioneering scientific technique was used in the 1936 trial of Dr Buck Ruxton to identify positively the remains of the victims' heads?

48 In which city did the strangler Samuel Morgan murder his fifteen-year-old victim Mary Hagan in 1940?

49 Of which form of relaxation therapy was the strangler, Joseph Clark, convicted of the 1928 murder of his former landlady Alice Fontaine, an amateur exponent?

50 When Frederick Field strangled his victim in a flat in Clapham in 1936, from which branch of the services was he a deserter?

51 How did the strangler Alfred Arthur Rouse attempt, almost incidentally, to render unrecognizable the body of his victim, on 6 November 1930?

52 What relation was his victim to the murderer Sidney Harry Fox, who was hanged in 1930?

53 In which county, in 1930, did the murderer Alfred Arthur Rouse first strangle, then attempt to render unrecognizable, the body of his victim?

54 What important classic clue, inadvertently left at the scene of the crime in 1959, was instrumental in confirming Patrick Joseph Byrne's involvement in the death of a young woman.

55 In which county did the murder of Ruby Keen by Leslie Stone take place in 1937?

56 What method of mutilation did strangler Styllou Pantopiou Christofi use on the corpse of her victim, in 1954, presumably in an attempt to disguise her crime?

57 What had Wills Eugene Boshears used to strangle Jean Constable in his flat at Great Dunmow, Essex, in 1961?

58 Damage to which delicate bone in the throat is almost invariably an indication of strangulation?

59 In which country, to which he had fled following his murder of schoolgirl Margaret Spevick in 1954, was William Sanchez de Pina Hepper arrested?

60 What type of prosecution evidence induced Leslie Stone to change his account of events leading to Ruby Keen's death, at his Old Bailey trial in 1937?

Question Rating (R3)

61 In 1959, what did the killer Patrick Joseph Byrne leave at the death scene, causing the police to ponder whether it was the work of a madman or a sick joke?

62 Of which of the armed services was Edward Thomas Lee, who admitted strangling his girlfriend Vera Bicknell in 1942, a member?

63 Where precisely had the strangler Kiernan Kelly, an Irish vagrant, killed his victim William Boyd in 1983?

64 In the 1930 case, considering the condition of the remains of Alfred Arthur Rouse's victim, and the fact that the pathologist found that he was still alive when an attempt to render him unrecognizable was made, how can we be sure he was strangled to some point of incapacitation?

65 In 1901 Herbert John Bennett was executed for the murder of his wife in Yarmouth. With what was she strangled?

66 What, according to a contemporary newspaper article, allegedly in the prisoner's own words, was the motive which prompted murderer Chung Yi Miao to kill his victim in 1928?

67 What was the occupation of John McMann Mudie, the victim of the infamous 1946 'Chalkpit Murder'?

68 When Gordon Hay was convicted of the murder of Linda Peacock in 1968, he became the first murderer to be identified in Scotland by what, then novel, branch of forensic science?

69 What was the name of the hotel in which Sidney Harry Fox strangled his victim in 1929?

70 What was the relationship between the murderer Herbert John Bennett and parlourmaid Alice Meadows?

71 What was the nationality of Styllou Pantopiou Christofi's victim, whom she murdered in London in 1954?

72 What defence, subsequently rejected by the jury, did the strangler William Sanchez de Pina Hepper put forward at his 1954 trial at Lewes Assizes for the murder of a schoolgirl?

73 With what item of clothing did Mrs Edith Chubb kill Lilian Chubb, in her home at Broadstairs, Kent, in 1958?

74 What extraordinary defence did Wills Eugene Boshears offer at his trial, at the Essex Assizes in 1961, for the murder of Jean Constable?

75 What was the relationship between Isabella Ruxton and Dr Buck Ruxton, who murdered her in 1935?

76 In which type of establishment did the murderer known as 'Bible John' meet all his victims in the late 1960s?

77 What interesting coincidence links the post-mortem examinations of both Rachel Dobkin, the victim, and Harry Dobkin, her murderer, executed in 1943?

78 What is the technical name given to any piece of material used to strangle a victim?

79 For what reason is it alleged that the murderer Herbert John Bennett was deported from another country, only four days after arriving, around the turn of the century?

80 On the day he committed the murder, in 1929, Sidney Harry Fox renewed two insurance policies on his victim's life. For how long?

81 What motive was put forward, by the prosecution, at the trial of Dr Buck Ruxton, hanged in 1936?

82 Which classic clue helped identify and subsequently convict Harold Dorian Trevor of the murder of Mrs Theodora Greenhill in 1941?

83 Following the abduction and rape of a Girl Guide in 1960, the strangler Arthur Albert Jones had been interviewed along with about 5,000 other owners of a particular make of black car. Which make?

84 Why, allegedly, following the frenzied strangling, sexual assault and mutilation of his victim Stephanie Baird in 1959, did Patrick Joseph Byrne have so little blood on his clothes?

85 In which county did the famous 'Chalkpit Murder' occur in 1946?

86 What specific request by the police panicked Patrick Joseph Byrne into confessing to the killing of Stephanie Baird in 1959?

87 Why was Frederick Nodder, the murderer of schoolgirl Mona Tinsley, charged, convicted and sentenced only for her abduction, in early 1937?

88 What verdict, against the judge's direction, was returned in the trial of Edward Thomas Lee for the strangling of his girlfriend in 1942?

89 Out of what did the strangler Kiernan Kelly construct the ligature he used to kill William Boyd in London in 1983?

90 What was the occupation of Michael Lupo when, in 1986, he was arrested for a series of murders in London in the same year?

Question Rating (R4)

91 In 1934 what did murderer David Blake become, less than twenty-four hours after his crime?

92 The replica badge of which British Regiment was found at the scene of the murder of sixteen-year-old Nellie Trew on Eltham Common in 1918?

93 In what sort of institution had the strangler Gordon Hay been confined at the time of his offence in 1967?

94 In which town or city did the murderer Dr Buck Ruxton have his GP's practice at the time of his crime in 1935?

95 From which well-known debilitating disorder did Sidney Harry Fox's victims suffer?

96 Frederick Field, executed in 1936, had in 1933 been charged with the murder of a woman in 1931 and had been acquitted. What action by Field had prompted that charge to be brought, two years after the event?

97 What was the verdict in the trial of Mrs Sarah Harvey, charged with the murder of Mrs Frances Knight, whose mummified corpse was discovered in her house in Rhyl in 1960?

98 In common with very few other murderers, what did Sidney Harry Fox decline to do after being sentenced to death in 1930?

99 What item, connected with the murderer William Sanchez de Pina Hepper's current profession, was discovered near the body of his victim, Margaret Spevick, in 1954?

100 The hairs from which domestic animal, owned by murderer Derrick Edwardson, were found on the shoes and clothing of his victim, four-year-old Edwina Taylor, in 1957?

101 What was Timothy John Evans' occupation at the time of his arrest for murder in 1949?

102 In what type of location was the body of Doris Marmon, for whose murder Amelia Elizabeth Dyer was tried at the Old Bailey in 1896, found?

103 Peter Hogg was tried following the killing of his wife Margaret in 1984, her body having been discovered in a lake in Cumbria over seven years after her death. Why had the police been searching the lake around that time?

104 How many women did the notorious strangler 'Bible John' murder in the late 1960s?

105 What was the occupation of Frederick Nodder, executed for the murder of ten-year-old Mona Tinsley in 1937?

106 What was the name of the public house in Portsmouth where the manager, Mrs Rose Ada Robinson, was allegedly strangled by Harold Loughans in 1943?

107 What sentence was passed on the brutal killer Patrick Joseph Byrne following his conviction in 1960?

108 What was significant, historically, about the trial of Herbert John Bennett at the Old Bailey in 1901?

109 From which country, where he had been cared for by relatives, did the strangler Joseph Clark return in 1927, before subsequently murdering his former landlady, Alice Fontaine, in 1928?

110 For what crime had Arthur Albert Jones already started fourteen years' imprisonment, in 1961, when charged with the murder of eleven-year-old Brenda Nash, a year earlier?

111 When murderer Derrick Edwardson was sentenced to life imprisonment in 1957 for the murder of four-year-old Edwina Taylor, who had also been sexually assaulted, what did a letter from the victim's father ask of the Home Secretary?

112 From which country had Herbert John and Mary Jane Bennett been deported, around the turn of the century, after only four days in situ?

113 What had been the occupation of the strangler Percy Charles Anderson's victim, Edith Constance Drew-Bear, whom he murdered in 1934?

114 What unnerving event occurred at the execution of Herbert John Bennett, at Norwich Prison in 1901?

115 On which initial charge was the murderer Sidney Harry Fox arrested in 1929, while inquiries into a suspicious death continued?

116 From which regiment was strangler David Greenwood discharged on medical grounds in 1917?

117 At which prison was the convicted murderer Dr Buck Ruxton hanged in 1936.

118 What legal proceedings, heard in 1963, did Harold Loughans begin from prison?

119 What was the profession of Ruby Keen's fiancé at the time she was murdered by Leslie Stone in 1937?

120 For which country had the murderer William Sanchez de Pina Hepper once been a spy in Spain?

Question Rating (R5)

121 At his trial for the murder in Folkestone, Kent, in 1943 of Caroline Ellen Trayler what was the sentence passed on Dennis Edmund Leckey?

122 Where was the body of four-year-old Edwina Taylor, strangled by Derrick Edwardson in 1957, eventually discovered.

123 When Chung Yi Miao strangled his victim in 1928 it was the first recorded murder in that part of the country for how many years?

124 What was the occupation of Frederick Field's victim, Beatrice Sutton, whom he strangled in 1936?

125 At which battle in the Great War had the subsequently convicted murderer, David Greenwood, been 'buried alive'?

126 At the trial of Peter Quinn in Glasgow, in 1932, for the 'domestic' murder of Chrissie Gall, what common household article was shown to have caused her death?

127 What was Leslie Stone's occupation, at the time he murdered Ruby Keen, in 1937?

128 Murderess Styllou Pantopiou Christofi, executed in 1954, had been acquitted of an earlier homicide in another country in 1925. What horrific method had Christofi used on her victim on that occasion?

129 Of what colour and material was the suit worn for the first time by murderer Leslie Stone when strangling Ruby Keen in 1937? (Material from the scene was later discovered in this new suit.)

130 What did the infamous strangler, Amelia Elizabeth Dyer, use to murder all of her victims?

131 What was the verdict in the 1984 trial of Peter Hogg, following the killing of his wife Margaret, whose remains had been found in a lake in Cumbria?

132 What household item, besides pieces of string, was found around the neck of Chung Yi Miao's victim?

133 What damning evidence led to the arrest of Herbert Leonard Mills and his subsequent trial for the murder of Mrs Mabel Tattershaw in 1951?

134 After strangling his victim, with what did Patrick Joseph Byrne decapitate the corpse?

135 The remains of murderer Dr Buck Ruxton's victims were wrapped in sheets of which newspaper?

136 At Harold Loughans' second trial for murder, in 1944, what physical disability threw doubt on his ability to have committed the crime?

137 What was used by lorry driver Harold Hagger to strangle a hitchhiker, Dagmar Peters, in Kent in 1946?

138 At Edward Thomas Lee's trial in 1942, from which medical condition was it argued that his victim Vera Bicknell had suffered, thus contributing to her own death?

139 For what offence was Mrs Sarah Harvey eventually sentenced to fifteen months' imprisonment, following her trial for the murder of Mrs Frances Knight whose mummified corpse was discovered at the defendant's home in 1960?

140 What had the subsequently convicted murderer James Pollard splashed on the body of his victim Zoe Wade, in her council flat, before setting fire to the apartment, in 1984?

141 What did the strangler Joseph Clark use to murder his former landlady Alice Fontaine in 1928?

142 What was the nickname by which Isabella Ruxton, victim of Dr Buck Ruxton, was known locally?

143 Following his murder of Emily Yeomans in 1934, which incriminating item of property, belonging to the victim, did David Blake give to an acquaintance?

144 In the 1934 case what had the strangler Percy Charles Anderson used to murder his victim, Edith Constance Drew-Bear after shooting her in the head had failed to kill her?

145 How many people did the convicted killer Kiernan Kelly tell police he had slain over thirty years?

146 In which newspaper did murderer Herbert Leonard Mills announce the 'discovery' by him of his victim's body in 1951?

147 In 1928 the subsequently convicted strangler Sidney Harry Fox had been sentenced to fifteen months' imprisonment. For what crime?

148 To which newspaper in the 1960s did Harold Loughans offer an article admitting his responsibility for strangling Mrs Rose Ada Robinson in 1943?

149 Why did Dennis Edmund Leckey, sentenced for the 1943 murder of Caroline Ellen Trayler, escape the hangman's noose?

150 A search of murderer Derrick Edwardson's workplace locker, following the death of his four-year-old victim Edwina Taylor in 1957, revealed what incriminating evidence?

CHAPTER THREE
THE SHOOTERS

Question Rating (R1)

1 What was historically significant about the execution of Ruth Ellis, on 13 July 1955, for the murder of David Blakely?

> **2** In a famous 1952 case, who is alleged to have uttered the fateful words 'Let him have it, Chris'?

3 In which small Berkshire town did a famous massacre take place in 1987?

> **4** At a lay-by on which road in Bedfordshire did the 1961 murder of Michael Gregsten by James Hanratty take place?

5 What was the name of the man who, in 1987, having perpetrated a massacre in a small Berkshire town, shot himself dead before he could be arrested?

> **6** How did the killer Samuel James Furnace attempt to conceal the true identity of the body of his victim, Walter Spatchett, after shooting him in Camden Town, London, in 1933?

7 What was the name of the female victim in the infamous 1827 'Red Barn Murder', perhaps one of the most celebrated British murder cases?

8 What was the nationality of Lock Ah Tam convicted of the 1925 murder, by shooting, of his wife and two daughters?

9 What natural phenomenon, particularly associated with London at that time, aided the escape of the murderer Thomas Henry Orrock, following his shooting dead of George Cole in Dalston, in 1882?

10 Is the barrel of a shotgun 'grooved' to the right or to the left?

11 In the shooting at the Barn Restaurant in 1972, which man was tried twice and finally acquitted of the murder of Mrs Muriel Patience?

12 After whom or what was the sensational 1926 'Stella Maris' shooting case named?

13 When George Gutteridge was murdered in Essex in 1927, by Frederick Guy Browne and William Henry Kennedy, which parts of the victim's body had been deliberately shot, for apparently superstitious reasons?

14 What was the occupation of David Blakely, shot dead by Ruth Ellis in London in 1955?

15 What nationality was the murderer Guenther Fritz Erwin Podola who, in 1959, shot dead Raymond Purdy in a block of flats in London?

16 In a famous 1952 case, who fired the actual shot which killed PC Sidney Miles, of whose murder Christopher Craig and Derek Bentley were subsequently convicted?

17 What was the occupation of George Gutteridge, murdered by Frederick Guy Browne and William Henry Kennedy in a country lane, between Romford and Ongar in Essex, in 1927?

18 What was the name of the area in Bedfordshire in which the 1961 murder of Michael Gregsten by James Hanratty took place?

19 What was the nationality of Prince Ali Kamel Fahmy Bey, shot dead by his wife in London in 1923?

20 When Christopher Craig was arrested in 1952 for the murder of PC Sidney Miles, how had he sustained his recent injuries resulting in a fractured spine and forearm?

21 In which county did the shooting of cashier John Nisbett by John Alexander Dickman take place in 1910?

22 What was the nationality of Elizabeth Maud Jones, also known as Georgina Grayson, who, together with Karl Gustav Hulten, was convicted of the 1944 murder of London taxi driver George Heath?

23 What was the name of the man convicted of the infamous 1827 'Red Barn Murder'?

24 What was Ruth Ellis's occupation at the time she shot dead her lover, David Blakely, in 1955?

25 What was the occupation of murderer Karl Gustav Hulten who shot dead a London taxi driver in 1944?

26 What was the name of the female victim present at the time of the shooting of Michael Gregsten, by James Hanratty in 1961, who was subsequently raped and shot but lived to give evidence against him?

27 What was the nationality of Karl Gustav Hulten convicted and executed for the 1944 murder of London taxi driver, George Heath?

28 Where within the barn was the decomposing body of the female victim in the infamous 1827 murder case, the 'Red Barn Murder', found?

29 What was the motive behind the 1972 'Barn Restaurant' shooting of Mrs Muriel Patience?

30 What is the name given to the marks left on a bullet by the grooves of the gun barrel from which it is fired, which, by comparison with identical marks left on a 'test' bullet from the same gun, may establish the identity of a murder weapon?

Question Rating (R2)

31 What was the nickname by which Max Kassel, a Latvian shot dead in London in 1936, was generally known?

32 In what capacity had Ernest Brown been employed by his victim Frederick Morton, a cattle dealer, whom he shot dead in 1933?

33 What notable feature did the post-mortem examination reveal about the bullets used to kill cashier John Nisbett in 1910, for whose murder John Alexander Dickman was subsequently convicted and executed in the same year?

34 In which county was the farmhouse 'Moat Farm' where Samuel Herbert Dougal murdered Camille Holland in 1899?

35 Where was the revolver used in the 1961 murder of Michael Gregsten by James Hanratty subsequently discovered?

36 What was the nationality of Marie-Marguerite Fahmy who shot dead her husband Prince Ali Kamel Fahmy Bey in London in 1923?

37 In which area of the Home Counties did the 1952 murder of PC Sidney Miles take place, of which Christopher Craig and Derek Bentley were subsequently convicted?

38 What incriminating evidence was subsequently discovered in a London hotel room, previously occupied by James Hanratty, who was found guilty of the 1961 murder of Michael Gregsten?

39 What type of weapon was used by Michael George Hart to shoot dead bank cashier Angela Woolliscroft in Richmond, Surrey, in 1976?

40 What was the occupation of Nathaniel Edgar, found fatally wounded in the drive of a house in Southgate, London, in 1948, after being shot by Donald George Thomas?

41 In which county did the murder of Kitty Breaks by her lover Frederick Rothwell Holt take place in 1919?

42 How did Alec de Antiquis come to be shot dead in a London street in 1947?

43 From which country's armed services had Alexander Campbell Mason, subsequently convicted of the 1923 London murder of taxi driver Jacob Dickey, deserted during the First World War?

44 What was Abraham 'Jack' Goldenberg's occupation at the time he murdered the cashier William Hall in 1924?

45 What mode of transport was Alec de Antiquis using when he was shot dead outside a shop in London in 1947?

46 What was the name given at the time to the 1944 murder case involving the shooting of taxi driver George Heath by Karl Gustav Hulten and Elizabeth Maud Jones, which referred to a physical characteristic of the victim?

47 What was the occupation of Arthur Wells, shot dead by John Williams at Eastbourne, Sussex, in October 1912?

48 Discovered in 1923, where exactly on their stud farm had Ernest Dyer left the body of his victim, Eric Gordon Tombe, whom he had killed in 1921?

49 Why did Samuel James Furnace, who murdered Walter Spatchett in Camden Town, London, in 1933, never stand trial for that offence?

50 Where did the 1881 murder of Isaac Frederick Gold, a coin dealer, by Percy Mapleton take place, giving it the dubious distinction then of being only the second murder to occur in such a place in this country?

51 What was the occupation of Cecil Maltby who shot dead his lover Alice Hilda Middleton in 1922, in the flat above his London shop?

52 What was the relationship between Eric Gordon Tombe and his killer Ernest Dyer, who shot him at their stud farm in 1921?

53 When Howard Wilson shot dead two men in a Scottish city following a robbery in 1969, what had initially caused him to be recognized by a policeman?

> **54** In which county did the 1925 murders of his wife and two daughters by Lock Ah Tam take place?

55 In which part of the country did the infamous 'Red Barn Murder' of 1827 take place?

> **56** What piece of laboratory equipment is used to examine bullets to ascertain whether they have been fired from the same weapon?

57 In which county had the 1972 'Barn Restaurant' shooting of Mrs Muriel Patience taken place?

> **58** In which county did the sensational 'Stella Maris' shooting case take place in 1926?

59 What sort of illegal enterprise were Frederick Guy Browne and William Henry Kennedy engaged in when their victim, George Gutteridge, happened across them in 1927?

> **60** What was the nationality of the two men, Marian Grondkowski and Henryk Malinowski, convicted at the Old Bailey of the 1945 murder, in London, of an Armenian criminal, Ruben Martirosoff?

Question Rating (R3)

61 In the 1961 murder case, in which James Hanratty was convicted of the murder of Michael Gregsten, what notable physical feature did the killer have, which the female witness to the crime particularly remembered?

62 In which county was 'Saxton Grange', the farmhouse where Ernest Brown shot dead his former employer, Frederick Morton in 1933?

63 When Christopher Craig and Derek Bentley were arrested for the murder of PC Sidney Miles in 1952, what were their respective ages?

64 What was the occupation of Elizabeth Maud Jones, also known as Georgina Grayson, who, together with Karl Gustav Hulten, was convicted of the 1944 murder of London taxi driver George Heath?

65 What was the motive behind Samuel James Furnace's attempt to conceal the true identity of the body of his victim, Walter Spatchett, whom he had shot dead in Camden Town, London, in 1933?

66 What was the occupation of George Cole, shot dead in December 1882 by Thomas Henry Orrock, in Dalston, London?

67 Which natural feature of the weather aided James Blomfield Rush in both his murder of Isaac and Jermy Jermy in November 1848 and his subsequent escape?

68 What very unusual event led to a search of the 'Red Barn', in the case of the same name, in 1828, and the discovery of the victim's decomposed body, before it was even known that she had been murdered?

69 In which seaside town was James Hanratty, subsequently convicted of the 1961 murder of Michael Gregsten, arrested?

70 Which type of firearm had been used to murder the female victim in the infamous 'Red Barn Murder' case of 1827?

71 What was the occupation of Michael Gregsten, shot dead in a lay-by in 1961 by James Hanratty?

72 In which Scottish city did Howard Wilson shoot dead two men following a robbery in 1969?

73 In which regiment of the British Army had the murderer Samuel Herbert Dougal previously served for a number of years?

74 In the 1932 case involving Mrs Elvira Barney, accused of shooting dead her lover, Michael Scott Stephen, at her home in Knightsbridge, London, which make of firearm had been used?

75 What was the occupation of Miss Elizabeth McLindon who was found dead from a gunshot wound at a house in Belgravia, London, in 1946?

76 From which country had the subsequently convicted murderer Guenther Fritz Erwin Podola been deported in 1958 after serving a prison sentence for burglary and theft?

77 Which make of firearm had been used in the 1927 murder of George Gutteridge in Essex, of which Frederick Guy Browne and William Henry Kennedy were subsequently convicted?

78 At a branch of which bank, in November 1976, at Richmond, Surrey, was Angela Woolliscroft shot dead by Michael George Hart?

79 What connection did Donald George Thomas, convicted of the 1948 murder by shooting of Nathaniel Edgar, have with the armed services?

80 During the course of what type of illegal activity was his victim, William Hall, shot dead by murderer Abraham 'Jack' Goldenberg, in 1924?

81 Which Territorial army rank had been held by Frederick Rothwell Holt, who murdered his mistress Kitty Breaks in 1919?

82 Outside which type of shop in London, relevant to his murder, was Alec de Antiquis shot dead in 1947?

83 What was the nickname of Alexander Campbell Mason convicted of the 1923 murder of taxi driver, Jacob Dickey, in London?

84 In which county did the murder of Florence Dennis, by her ex-lover James Canham Read, take place in 1894?

85 What mode of transport had the subsequently convicted murderers, Karl Gustav Hulten and Elizabeth Maud Jones, used to travel around at night in 1944?

86 In which county was the stud farm on which Ernest Dyer killed Eric Gordon Tombe in 1921?

87 With which relative's 1981 murder was Mrs Muriel McCullough jointly charged, with others, the following year?

88 What was the occupation of Samuel James Furnace who killed Walter Spatchett, in Camden Town, London, in 1933?

89 Where exactly in the flat above his London shop, did Cecil Maltby leave the decomposing body of his victim, Alice Hilda Middleton, for several months after shooting her dead in 1922?

90 When Horace George Rayner shot dead seventy-five-year-old William Whiteley in London in 1907, what relationship did he claim to have had to his victim?

Question Rating (R4)

91 What was the profession of James Blomfield Rush who shot dead Isaac Jermy and his son Jermy, in November 1848?

92 How did the defendant, in the infamous 'Red Barn murder' of 1827, assert, unsuccessfully, that his female victim had died?

93 In what sort of conveyance was the body of an Armenian criminal, Ruben Martirosoff, discovered in Kensington, London, in 1945?

94 What was the occupation of the two men shot dead by Howard Wilson in Scotland, in December 1969, following a robbery?

95 Alfonso Francis Austin Smith, whom a jury subsequently found not guilty of murdering John Derham in the sensational 1926 'Stella Maris' case, had been to the same famous public school as Derham; which school?

96 What was the occupation of Frederick Guy Browne, convicted with William Henry Kennedy of the 1927 murder of George Gutteridge, in Essex?

97 What was the occupation of Lock Ah Tam, convicted of the 1925 murder by shooting of his wife and two daughters?

98 How did Guenther Fritz Erwin Podola come to be discovered in a telephone box in London, shortly before shooting dead Raymond Purdy, in 1959?

99 In what type of business concern was John Nisbett, shot dead in 1910 while on his way to deliver wages from their Newcastle office, employed as a cashier?

100 In which 'obvious' location did the police immediately find the name and address of the murderer David George Thomas, subsequently convicted of the 1948 shooting of Nathaniel Edgar?

101 In which county did the murder of cashier William Hall, shot dead by Abraham 'Jack' Goldenberg in 1924, take place?

102 Although he was known to be the culprit, why had it not been possible to charge Ernest Dyer with the 1921 killing of Eric Gordon Tombe when the latter's remains were discovered in 1923?

103 William Whiteley, shot dead in his London office by Horace George Rayner in 1907, was the founder of Britain's first what?

104 What type of weapon did the murderer James Blomfield Rush use on his victims Isaac and Jermy Jermy, in November 1848?

105 In 1969, two men were shot dead in a Scottish city by Howard Wilson, following a robbery at what type of premises?

106 From which penal institution had Roger Marcel Vernon, alias George Lacroix, convicted of the 1936 murder by shooting of Max Kassel in London, escaped in 1927?

107 From the time of her disappearance and her murder by Samuel Herbert Dougal in 1899, how long, approximately, was it before the body of Camille Holland was discovered?

108 How many men were finally convicted of the murder by shooting of Alec de Antiquis outside a London shop in 1947?

109 Where in London was James Canham Read, who murdered his ex-mistress Florence Dennis in 1894, employed as a clerk?

110 What was the nickname given by the press to John Williams, convicted of the 1912 murder of Arthur Wells in Eastbourne, Sussex, because of the manner in which he was moved to and from the courthouse?

111 What strange incident led to the discovery of the body of Eric Gordon Tombe, shot dead in 1921 by Ernest Dyer at their stud farm?

112 In which seaside town was Samuel James Furnace, the killer of Walter Spatchett in Camden Town, London, in 1933, eventually arrested?

113 What revelation by Florence Dennis, in 1894, prompted her murder by her ex-lover James Canham Read?

114 Why, following his arrest for the murder of George Cole in Dalston, London, in 1882, which was witnessed by two women, was the culprit Thomas Henry Orrock released without being charged?

115 What was the relationship between James Blomfield Rush and one of his victims, Isaac Jermy, whom he shot dead in 1848?

116 What type of evidence, leading to public disquiet about the verdict, was the mainstay of the prosecution case in the 1910 trial of John Alexander Dickman, subsequently executed for the murder by shooting of a cashier?

117 Which item of clothing, which led to his identification and arrest, did two female witnesses claim to have seen the culprit Thomas Henry Orrock wearing, as he shot dead George Cole in Dalston, London, in 1882?

118 What had happened to the defendant Lock Ah Tam in 1918 which, it was argued at his trial for murder, had led him to shoot dead his wife and two daughters in 1925?

119 In 1974 whom was John Brook eventually convicted of murdering, and where, after another man had been twice tried for the offence and finally acquitted?

120 What had prompted the ill feeling between Alfonso Francis Austin Smith and John Derham which resulted in Derham's death in the sensational 1926 'Stella Maris' case?

Question Rating (R5)

121 Where was William John Clarke at the time he was charged with the 1966 murder of his former associate, John White?

122 What connection with the armed services did the two men Marian Grondkowski and Henryk Malinowski, subsequently convicted of the 1945 murder in London of Ruben Martirosoff, have?

123 What had been the occupation of George Ellis in 1950 when he married Ruth Ellis, who was subsequently convicted of the murder, by shooting, of David Blakely in 1955?

124 Which make of firearm was used by Ruth Ellis to murder David Blakely in London in 1955?

125 In which county did the murderer James Blomfield Rush shoot dead Isaac Jermy and his son Jermy in November 1848?

126 At the time he murdered bank cashier Angela Woolliscroft in Richmond, Surrey, in 1976, Michael George Hart was already 'wanted' for an attempted murder; in which country?

127 What was the occupation of Alec de Antiquis, shot dead outside a shop in London in 1947?

128 Where was the identity parade held, in Yorkshire, in 1951, at which the murderer Alfred Moore was picked out by one of his victims?

129 What was the occupation of Edward Lawrence charged with the 1908 murder of his mistress Ruth Hadley in Wolverhampton, and brilliantly defended by his counsel Edward Marshall Hall?

130 In which county did the 1981 murder, involving Mrs Muriel McCullough and others as the perpetrators, take place?

131 What was the occupation of Arthur Boyce, convicted of the 1946 murder by shooting of Miss Elizabeth McLindon at a house in Belgravia, London?

132 What type of 'authority' did the police eventually use, in 1923, to enter the London shop of Cecil Maltby and discover the decomposing body of his victim Alice Hilda Middleton?

133 What enterprising piece of detective work by police Sergeant Cobb, over a year after the 1882 murder of George Cole by Thomas Henry Orrock in Dalston, London, led to the conviction and execution of the murderer?

134 What forensic evidence, despite written notes to the contrary, tends to discount the possibility that Alice Hilda Middleton committed suicide in the flat, above the London shop, of Cecil Maltby in 1922?

135 What was the nickname of Ruben Martirosoff, an Armenian with a criminal record, found shot to death in Kensington, London, in 1945?

136 How was the forensic evidence, relating to the weapon used by William John Clarke to kill his former associate John White in 1966, discovered by police?

137 What was the occupation of Alice Hilda Middleton's husband, who was out of the country when his wife was shot dead by Cecil Maltby in 1922?

138 Into what type of building had Thomas Henry Orrock attempted to gain entry, just prior to his being discovered and shooting dead George Cole in Dalston, London, in 1882?

139 What was the profession of Percy Mapleton, who murdered and robbed coin dealer Isaac Frederick Gold in 1881?

140 In what dubious occupation had Max Kassel been engaged, in London, just prior to his death by shooting in 1936?

141 What was the name of the stud farm on which Eric Gordon Tombe was shot dead by Ernest Dyer in 1921?

142 In which county did the 1947 murders of Percy and Alice Baker by John Edward Gartside take place?

143 Which type of weapon was used when John Derham was shot dead in the sensational 1926 'Stella Maris' case?

144 What was the real name of the professional burglar John Williams, subsequently convicted in 1912 of the murder of Arthur Wells in Eastbourne, Sussex, in the same year?

145 Which make of firearm had been used by Donald George Thomas, subsequently convicted of murder, to shoot his victim Nathaniel Edgar in Southgate, London, in 1948?

146 How many guns did Lock Ah Tam use in murdering his wife and two daughters in 1925?

147 What were the occupations of the two men shot dead by Alfred Moore, near a remote farm in Yorkshire in July 1951?

148 Which make of firearm was used by the killer Samuel James Furnace on victim Walter Spatchett, whom he shot dead in Camden Town, London, in 1933?

149 In which part of the country was the body of John White, of whose murder William John Clarke was eventually convicted, discovered in 1966 (although this was apparently not where he had been shot)?

150 What was the occupation of the murderer Alfred Moore, who shot dead two men near a remote farm in Yorkshire in July 1951?

CHAPTER FOUR

THE BLUDGEONERS

Question Rating (R1)

1 Which famous figure did Kenneth Halliwell batter to death in a flat they shared in Islington, London, in 1967?

2 In which city did the celebrated 1931 murder of Mrs Julia Wallace, who was battered to death at her home with a blunt instrument, take place?

3 Where, in London in 1911, was the body of Leon Beron found, of whose murder Stinie Morrison was subsequently convicted?

4 What nationality was Franz Müller, who murdered Thomas Briggs, a chief bank clerk, in London in 1864?

5 At the 1975 inquest into the death of victim Sandra Rivett what, now famous, verdict was returned?

6 What was the occupation of William Herbert Wallace, who was convicted of the 1931 battering to death of his wife, Julia, at their home?

7 In which city in 1908 was Miss Marion Gilchrist beaten to death at her home, a murder for which Oscar Slater was later sentenced to death?

8 What nationality was shared by the victim Leon Beron and Stinie Morrison, the man subsequently convicted of his 1911 murder in London?

9 In what type of establishment, in London, was Lady White battered to death by Henry Julius Jacoby in 1922?

10 What was John Norman Holmes Thorne's occupation at the time he murdered Elsie Cameron, in December 1924?

11 For which famous company did William Herbert Wallace, convicted of the 1931 murder of his wife Julia, work?

12 How had the murderer Patrick Albert Mahon tried to avoid discovery of the body of his victim Emily Beilby Kaye, whom he had killed in 1924?

13 By what name, and why, did the murderess Margaret Allen, convicted of the 1948 killing of a local eccentric, Nancy Chadwick, like to be called?

14 In which city did the subsequently convicted murderer Ronald True batter and asphyxiate his victim Mrs Gertrude Yates in her basement flat in 1922?

15 What was the occupation of Mrs Gertrude Yates, murdered in her basement flat in 1922 by Ronald True?

16 What item, found by his wife in one of his pockets, led police to the discovery of incriminating items belonging to the murderer Patrick Albert Mahon, whose victim, Emily Beilby Kaye, was killed in 1924?

17 In which city did the trial of Oscar Slater, accused of murdering Miss Marion Gilchrist at her home in 1908, take place?

18 How was the murderer Horace William Manton, who killed his wife Rene Manton in Bedfordshire in 1943, more usually known?

19 In which city was the fugitive Franz Müller arrested in 1864 following his murder, in the same year, of Thomas Briggs, a chief bank clerk, in London?

20 Which child's toy, found near the body of victim Henry Smith in 1896, helped lead to the subsequent conviction of Henry Fowler and Albert Milsom for his murder?

21 In what type of building, near Eastbourne, were the remains of Emily Beilby Kaye, murdered in 1924 by Patrick Albert Mahon, discovered?

22 In which county did the murder of Elsie Cameron by John Norman Holmes Thorne take place, in December 1924?

23 What nationality was Oscar Slater, subsequently convicted of the murder of Miss Marion Gilchrist at her home in 1908?

24 Inside what was the body of Christina Bradfield, savagely battered to death in Liverpool by George Ball in 1913, sewn to hide it prior to disposal?

25 In 1911 what mutilations were found on the face of the dead Leon Beron, of whose murder Stinie Morrison was subsequently convicted?

26 Which famous writer campaigned vigorously for an enquiry into the case of Oscar Slater, serving a sentence of life imprisonment for the murder of Miss Marion Gilchrist in 1908?

27 In which city was the decomposing body of Vivian Messiter discovered in 1929, for whose murder William Henry Podmore was eventually executed in 1930?

28 What was the occupation of Sandra Rivett, beaten to death in Belgravia, London, in 1974, whose murderer has not, to date, been apprehended?

29 When Franz Müller beat seventy-year-old chief bank clerk Thomas Briggs to death in 1864, he committed the first murder, in Britain, in which particular type of location?

30 What was the occupation of Henry Julius Jacoby, subsequently convicted of the murder, in London, of Lady White in 1922?

Question Rating (R2)

31 Whom did the twenty-nine-year-old labourer George Carter bludgeon to death at Cowbridge, Glamorganshire, in January 1960, for which crime he was sentenced to imprisonment for life?

32 In which university city did the 1931 killing of Mrs Annie Louise Kempson, battered to death by subsequently convicted Henry Daniel Seymour, take place?

33 In what sort of club was William Herbert Wallace on the evening before his wife's death in 1931, when he received a mysterious message asking him to meet a stranger the following day, on business, thus keeping him away from home around the time his wife Julia was battered to death?

34 Which military rank did the murderer Ronald True pass himself off as having at the time of his killing Mrs Gertrude Yates in her basement flat in 1922?

35 Where in 1924 was the murderer Patrick Albert Mahon eventually apprehended by the police?

36 What age was the murderer Henry Julius Jacoby, executed for the brutal killing of Lady White in London in 1922?

37 In what type of location in Bedfordshire was the body of Mrs Rene Manton, murdered by her husband Horace William Manton in 1943, discovered?

38 What was the motive behind the 1933 murder of eighty-year-old Joseph Bedford by Frederick William Parker and Albert Probert?

39 What was unusual about the mode of dress of the killer Margaret Allen, who was convicted of the 1948 murder of local eccentric Nancy Chadwick?

40 In what type of location was the body of Christina Bradfield, savagely battered to death in Liverpool by George Ball in 1913, eventually found?

41 In which country was Oscar Slater, subsequently convicted of the murder of Miss Marion Gilchrist at her home in 1908, when British police officers caught up with him?

42 What was the profession of Leon Beron, found beaten to death in London in 1911, of whose murder Stinie Morrison was subsequently convicted?

43 In what type of building was the decomposing body of Vivian Messiter discovered in 1929, for whose murder William Henry Podmore was eventually executed in 1930?

44 In which seaside town did eighteen-year-old George Percy Stoner bludgeon his victim, Francis Rattenbury, to death in the sensational 1935 murder case?

45 What was the apparent motive for the murder of Francis Rattenbury by his eighteen-year-old employee George Percy Stoner, at his home in 1935?

46 To which article of clothing did the convicted killer, Franz Müller subsequently lend his name, following its prominence in his 1864 trial for the murder of Thomas Briggs, a seventy-year-old chief bank clerk?

47 What was the name of the lonely stretch of shingle, on the coast near Eastbourne, where seventeen-year-old Irene Munro was battered to death in 1920 by Jack Alfred Field and William Thomas Gray?

48 To which drug was Ronald True, convicted of the 1922 murder of Mrs Gertrude Yates, addicted?

49 How did Patrick Albert Mahon, subsequently convicted of the 1924 murder of Emily Beilby Kaye, say his victim had died?

50 What was the occupation of seventeen-year-old Irene Munro, battered to death near Eastbourne in 1920, by Jack Alfred Field and William Thomas Gray?

51 In his home in which city did the 1896 murder of Henry Smith, of which Henry Fowler and Albert Milsom were subsequently convicted, take place?

52 Although her death was eventually from asphyxia, with what blunt instrument had the murderer Ronald True savagely beaten his victim Mrs Gertrude Yates about the head, in her basement flat in 1922?

53 What had been the occupation of Henry Daniel Seymour at the time he battered Mrs Annie Louise Kempson to death, at her home, in 1931?

54 What was the occupation of Horace William Manton, convicted of the 1943 murder of his wife Rene Manton, in Bedfordshire?

55 Where in Britain did the 1889 murder of London clerk Edwin Rose, by John Watson Laurie, take place?

56 What was the occupation of Franz Müller who murdered chief bank clerk Thomas Briggs, in London in 1864?

57 In the kitchen of what type of establishment, in Oxfordshire, was fifty-five-year-old widow Sarah Blake, murdered in 1922 by Jack Hewett?

58 With what implement had murderer Franz Müller beaten to death his victim, Thomas Briggs a seventy-year-old chief bank clerk, in London in 1864?

59 Where had seventeen-year-old Irene Munro, battered to death near Eastbourne in 1920 by Jack Alfred Field and William Thomas Gray, been born?

60 What was the motive for the battering to death of Henry Smith at his home in 1896, by Henry Fowler and Albert Milsom?

Question Rating (R3)

61 In which branch of the armed services, in 1915, was Ronald True, subsequently convicted of the murder of Mrs Gertrude Yates, badly injured?

62 What was the occupation of Patrick Albert Mahon, convicted of the murder of Emily Beilby Kaye in 1924?

63 With what implement did the murderer Henry Julius Jacoby batter to death Lady White in London in 1922?

64 What was the popular contemporary name of the crime relating to the discovery of the then unidentified body of Mrs Rene Manton in Bedfordshire in 1943?

65 What was the occupation of Elsie Cameron, brutally murdered by John Norman Holmes Thorne in December 1924?

66 What was the profession of Stinie Morrison, convicted of the 1911 murder of Leon Beron in London?

67 What was the nickname of the casual labourer Herbert Ayres, beaten to death in Hertfordshire in 1931 by William Shelley and Oliver Newman?

68 In what particular type of building was murderer Ronald True arrested in 1922, within hours of his killing of Mrs Gertrude Yates?

69 What was the occupation of both William Shelley and Oliver Newman, convicted of the 1931 murder in Hertfordshire of casual labourer Herbert Ayres?

70 What was the motive behind the murder of Elsie Cameron by John Norman Holmes Thorne in December 1924?

71 What was the occupation of George Ball, subsequently convicted of the brutal murder of Christina Bradfield in Liverpool in 1913?

72 What was the murder weapon used to bludgeon to death seventy-one-year-old Leonard Moules during a robbery at his shop in East London in 1942, for whose murder George Silverosa and Samuel Dashwood were subsequently convicted?

73 As what was the eighteen-year-old murderer George Percy Stoner employed by his victim Francis Rattenbury, whom he bludgeoned to death at his home in 1935?

74 What items, purchased before he murdered his victim Emily Beilby Kaye in 1924, indicated a degree of premeditation on the part of her killer, Patrick Albert Mahon?

75 Where had William Shelley and Oliver Newman left the body of their victim, Herbert Ayres, beaten to death in 1931 in Hertfordshire?

76 What was the occupation of Emily Beilby Kaye, murdered by Patrick Albert Mahon in 1924?

77 What implement had William Henry Podmore used to batter Vivian Messiter to death at his workplace in 1928?

78 During the Second World War what did Margaret Allen, subsequently convicted of the 1948 murder of Nancy Chadwick, work as?

79 Why was John Norman Holmes Thorne's explanation that the woman he had murdered in December 1924, Elsie Cameron, had in fact hanged herself from a beam, found to be fatally flawed?

80 What were the nicknames of the two murderers William Shelley and Oliver Newman, convicted of the 1931 murder of Herbert Ayres?

81 In which county did the 1948 murder of local eccentric Nancy Chadwick, by Margaret Allen, take place?

82 How had the killer James Roland Robertson murdered his victim, Catherine McCluskey, on the outskirts of Glasgow in 1950?

83 What was the occupation of George Newberry, murdered near Southampton in 1964 by George Ernest Sykes and John William Stoneley?

84 What was the nationality of Eyyup Celal, convicted of the 1958 murder of prostitute Margaret Brindley?

85 Mrs Gertrude Yates and Olive Young were murdered by Ronald True in a basement flat in 1922. What was the connection between these women?

86 In which county did the murder of eighty-year-old Joseph Bedford by Frederick William Parker and Albert Probert take place in 1933?

87 With what, according to his own admission, had the murderer Horace William Manton bludgeoned to death his wife, Rene Manton, in 1943?

88 In what type of conveyance was the body of Christina Bradfield, savagely beaten to death by George Ball in Liverpool in 1913, subsequently taken away for disposal by her murderer and his assistant, Samuel Angeles Elltoft?

89 With what did the murderer Eric Jones admit he had battered Mrs June Cook, who was found lying beside a car in 1967 and who subsequently died in hospital?

90 What was the occupation of Bryn Masterman, tried at Nottingham Crown Court in 1987 for the murder of his first wife Janet, at their home, over twenty years previously?

Question Rating (R4)

91 In which county did Philip Henry kill Miss Flora Jane Gilligan, found murdered outside her home in 1953?

92 Information from whom prompted police to investigate and charge Bryn Masterman in 1987 with the murder, at their home, of his first wife Janet over twenty years previously?

93 What was the profession, before his retirement, of Francis Rattenbury, bludgeoned to death at his home in 1935 by eighteen-year-old George Percy Stoner?

94 What had the murderer Ronald True left on the sideboard of his victim Mrs Gertrude Yates, whom he had killed in her basement flat in 1922, which immediately gave police a clue to his identity?

95 In what type of shop, in East London, was seventy-one-year-old Leonard Moules bludgeoned to death by George Silverosa and Samuel Dashwood during the course of a robbery in 1942?

96 What was the occupation of murderer James Roland Robertson, who killed his victim Catherine McCluskey on the outskirts of Glasgow in 1950?

97 In which county did the 1926 murder of Mrs Lily Waterhouse by Louie Calvert take place?

98 In which city, in 1889, did the trial of John Watson Laurie for the murder of Edwin Rose in the same year take place?

99 When William Brittle was convicted of the 1964 murder of Peter Thomas what, in the opinion of the pathologist, had caused the victim's death?

100 When arrested for the murder of fifty-five-year-old widow Sarah Blake, in Oxfordshire in 1922, to what modern social influence did her killer, Jack Hewett, attribute his crime?

101 What nationality was Marguerite Diblanc, convicted of the 1872 murder of her employer, Madame Marie Riel, in Park Lane, London?

102 What was the occupation of the Victorian murderer John Selby Watson, who murdered his wife Anne in London in 1871?

103 When Frederick and Maria Manning were executed in London in 1847 for the murder, in the same year, of Irish dock worker Patrick O'Connor, what dress material, worn by Maria, immediately became unfashionable?

104 What murder weapon, found under the floor of the defendants' hut, had been used by William Shelley and Oliver Newman to kill the casual labourer Herbert Ayres, in Hertfordshire in 1931?

105 In what type of building did the 1933 murder of eighty-year-old Joseph Bedford by Frederick William Parker and Albert Probert take place?

106 What murder weapon had Henry Daniel Seymour used on his victim, Mrs Annie Louise Kempson, in battering her to death at her home in 1931?

107 Where were the two murderers of eighty-year-old Joseph Bedford, Frederick William Parker and Albert Probert, found by the police a few hours after the discovery of the victim's body in 1933?

108 Two pieces of evidence were very important in the case against Horace William Manton who murdered his wife Rene in 1943. One was her fingerprint, which established the identity of her body. What was the second, relating to the murderer?

109 Nancy Chadwick, a local eccentric, was battered to death by Margaret Allen in 1948. What had the murderer used as a weapon?

110 In what type of sport had Horace William Manton, convicted of the 1943 murder of his wife Rene, once excelled?

111 A witness to the disposal of the body of Christina Bradfield's body in Liverpool in 1913, by her murderer George Ball and his assistant Samuel Angeles Elltoft, had been struck by a shutter from a shop, damaging which part of his clothing?

112 What had been the motive for the beating to death of Herbert Ayres in Hertfordshire, in 1931, by William Shelley and Oliver Newman?

113 How, according to his own statement, had the murderer Horace William Manton moved the dead body of his wife Rene from their home to its place of concealment in 1943?

114 What was the profession of William Henry Podmore, convicted in 1930 of the 1928 murder of Vivian Messiter at his workplace?

115 In which county did the 1967 murder of Mrs June Cook, found lying beside a car, take place?

116 What was the occupation of Philip Henry, convicted of the murder of Miss Flora Jane Gilligan at her home in 1953?

117 Under the influence of what or whom did eighteen-year-old murderer George Percy Stoner claim that he had bludgeoned to death Francis Rattenbury at his home in 1935?

118 What appeared to be the motive for William Henry Podmore battering Vivian Messiter to death, at his workplace, in 1928?

119 What articles of clothing, belonging to her victims, was Louie Calvert wearing when she was arrested in 1926 for the murder of Mrs Lily Waterhouse?

120 In what type of location was the body of Emma Sheard discovered in 1948, some seven years after her great-niece Mrs Winifred Hallaghan had killed and disposed of her body?

Question Rating (R5)

121 Newspaper articles concerning which other notorious murderer and dismemberer were found in the possession of John Norman Holmes Thorne after his killing of Elsie Cameron, in December 1924?

122 What was the nickname, given on account of his speed to Harry Michaelson, the cartoonist savagely beaten to death in London by Harry Lewis in 1948?

123 What was the sporting occupation of Linford Derrick who battered to death his friend's husband Arthur Wheeler, at the latter's home in West London in 1936?

124 Which household item proved to have been the murder weapon in the savage beating to death of the cartoonist Harry Michaelson by Harry Lewis in London in 1948?

125 What was the verdict in the 1987 trial of Bryn Masterman at Nottingham Crown Court, for the murder at their home of his first wife Janet over twenty years previously?

126 When Miss Flora Jane Gilligan was battered to death by Philip Henry at her home in 1953, how had the murderer attempted to make the crime appear an act of suicide?

127 With what implement did eighteen-year-old George Percy Stoner bludgeon his employer, Francis Rattenbury, to death at his home in 1935?

128 In which county did the 1952 murder of Mrs Alice Wiltshaw by Leslie Green take place?

129 For what devious purpose was Louie Calvert lodging at the home of her victim, Mrs Lily Waterhouse, in 1926, when she murdered her?

130 What uncommon occupation was shared by the subsequently convicted murderer San Dwe and his victim Sayed Ali, whose death took place in London in 1928?

131 What household implement had the murderer, Leslie Green, used to batter Mrs Alice Wiltshaw to death in 1952?

132 At his trial for the 1950 murder of Catherine McCluskey on the outskirts of Glasgow, how did the defendant James Roland Robertson attempt to explain his victim's death?

133 In what capacity had the murderer, Leslie Green, been employed by his victim Mrs Alice Wiltshaw, whom he battered to death in 1952?

134 In which county did the 1941 killing of Emma Sheard by her great-niece, Mrs Winifred Hallaghan, take place?

135 With what did murderer Michael Queripel beat his victim, Mrs Currell, to death in Potters Bar in 1955?

136 What was the occupation of Morris Arthur Clarke, convicted of the 1956 murder of farmer Arthur Johnson in Huntingdonshire?

137 In which particular type of location was the body of Edwin Rose, a London clerk murdered by John Watson Laurie, discovered in 1889?

138 Which classic piece of forensic evidence led to the arrest of Michael Queripel for the 1955 murder of Mrs Currell in Potters Bar?

139 In what capacity was murderess Marguerite Diblanc employed by her victim Madame Marie Riel, whom she killed in Park Lane, London, in 1872?

140 With what household implement did killer Jack Hewett admit to murdering fifty-five-year-old widow Sarah Blake in Oxfordshire in 1922?

141 In which city was the fugitive Marguerite Diblanc arrested after she had murdered her employer, Madame Marie Riel, in London in 1872?

142 What was the name given by the mystery telephone caller, on the evening before the murder, who allegedly lured William Herbert Wallace to a non-existent address, before battering to death his wife Julia, in her home, in 1931?

143 What age was Jack Hewett when he battered Sarah Blake, a fifty-five-year-old widow, to death in Oxfordshire in 1922?

144 What murder weapon did Kenneth Halliwell use to batter to death his famous lover, in the flat they shared in Islington, London, in 1967?

145 What was the non-existent address allegedly given to William Herbert Wallace in 1931, the search for which kept him away from his home around the time his wife was battered to death there?

146 What weapon did the Victorian murderer John Selby Watson use to batter to death his wife, Anne, in London in 1871?

147 How did Raymond Sidney Cook initially attempt to explain his wife June's death in 1967, when she was found lying beside a car?

148 In 1941, in what type of conveyance did Mrs Winifred Hallaghan convey the body of her great-aunt, Emma Sheard, to its place of concealment where it remained undiscovered for seven years?

149 In what type of location was the body of Mrs Currell discovered, after she was murdered in Potters Bar in 1955 by Michael Queripel?

150 What was the real surname of Oscar Slater, subsequently convicted of the murder of Miss Marion Gilchrist at her home in 1908?

CHAPTER FIVE

STABBERS AND SLASHERS

Question Rating (R1)

1 What was the occupation of Keith Blakelock, stabbed and hacked to death by unknown assailants, during a 1985 riot in North London?

2 Of the approximately 600 homicides every year in Great Britain, what roughly is the proportion of those committed with knives?

3 Which famous playwright, while in the same gaol, dedicated a ballad to the convicted murderer Charles Thomas Wooldridge, executed in 1896 for killing his wife Ellen, near Windsor, in the same year?

4 Name the two types of forensic classification of knife wounds.

5 What latest investigative technique, used in Britain for the first time in a murder inquiry, led to the 1961 arrest in London of Edwin Bush, for the murder of shop assistant Mrs Elsie May Batten in the same year?

6 What was the nationality of François Benjamin Courvoisier, who murdered his employer Lord William Russell in London in 1840?

7 In which county did the 1938 murder of Mrs Margaret Jane Dobson, of which twenty-one-year-old Robert Hoolhouse was eventually convicted, take place?

8 Which legendary Scotland Yard detective investigated the 1945 murder of Charles Walton, found near the Tudor village of Lower Quinton, Warwickshire, which was shrouded in mystery and overtones of witchcraft?

9 What was the occupation of Charles Thomas Wooldridge, convicted of the 1896 murder of his wife Ellen, for which he was executed at Reading Gaol?

10 What was the name of the North London housing estate where, during riots in 1985, Keith Blakelock was stabbed and hacked to death by a mob?

11 In 1765, Lord Byron, the uncle of the great poet, killed one of his friends, a Mr Chaworth, in a sword fight. Before which court, as was his right, was he tried?

12 What was the relationship between Colin George Saunders, a thirty-five-year-old chauffeur, and his killer, nineteen-year-old Stanley Wrenn, who murdered him at his bedsitter in Bromley, Kent, in 1969?

13 What was the nationality of Gunner Matthew Smith, convicted of the 1944 murder of lorry driver Charles Gilbey at 'Charlie Brown's' public house in Limehouse, London?

14 In which of the arts did the murderer Richard Dadd, who in 1843 killed his father Robert, eventually achieve fame?

15 Following the conviction of Peter Luckhurst for the 1980 murder of Miss Gwendoline Marshall in the village of Pluckley, Kent, what action was taken by some outraged local residents?

16 In which city did the celebrated 1862 murder of Jessie McPherson, a servant girl, by Jessie M'Lachlan, a former servant in the same household, take place?

17 What was the occupation of Emily Jane Dimmock, found dead with her throat cut in lodgings at Camden Town, North London, in 1907?

18 In which county did the famous 'Gorse Hall Murder', involving the stabbing to death of George Harry Storrs, take place in 1909?

19 What was the original nationality of second-hand car dealer Stanley Setty whose dismembered body was discovered in marshes following his murder, in 1949, by Brian Donald Hume?

20 In 1851 William Sheward murdered his wife Martha and then distributed pieces of her dismembered body around the city of Norwich. How did he come to be arrested over seventeen years after his crime?

21 What was the profession of convicted murderer Richard Prince, who stabbed his victim, William Terriss, to death in a London street in 1897?

22 In which county did the 1942 murder of Mrs Ellen Ann Symes, by Reginald Sidney Buckfield, take place?

23 What was the profession of William Terriss, stabbed to death by Richard Prince in a London street in 1897?

24 Which of his relatives did the Sikh, Suchnam Singh Sandhu, murder in Barking, Essex, in 1968?

25 To which of the armed services, from which he was a deserter, did Reginald Sidney Buckfield belong when he murdered Mrs Ellen Ann Symes in 1942, in a road near her home?

26 How had the dismembered torso of second-hand car dealer Stanley Setty, stabbed to death in 1949 by Brian Donald Hume, received a number of 'crash injury' broken bones after death?

27 What was the occupation of Raymond Summers, stabbed to death in a street in Holloway, North London, in 1958 by Ronald Henry Marwood?

28 In the sensational 1922 case whom did Frederick Bywaters stab to death in the street, leading to his execution for murder in the following year?

29 Near which Scottish town, already famous for other reasons, was the killer Stanley Eric Hobday arrested in 1933 following his murder of Charles William Fox in West Bromwich, Staffordshire, earlier that year?

30 What was the name of the public house frequented by Emily Jane Dimmock, found dead with her throat cut in lodgings at Camden Town, North London, in 1907? This public house featured prominently at the subsequent murder trial because of its mention on a picture postcard received by the victim.

Question Rating (R2)

31 What was the name of Frederick Bywaters' lover who was jointly charged with murder and executed on the same day in 1923?

> **32** For what reason was the murderer Arthur James Mahoney in the London flat of his victim, Georgina Hoffman, on the night of her murder in 1939?

33 Who was eventually convicted of the 1945 murder of Charles Walton, a seventy-four-year-old hedger, found with his throat stabbed and a hay-fork driven through his body, near the Tudor village of Lower Quinton, Warwickshire?

> **34** What was the name of the twenty-five-year-old artist who in 1907 was acquitted of the murder of Emily Jane Dimmock at her lodgings in Camden Town, North London, in the same year?

35 What was the occupation of William Donoghue, who stabbed to death his friend Thomas Meaney in his flat near Waterloo Station, London, in 1950?

> **36** What incriminating documents, written by the accused, helped lead to the conviction of Reginald Sidney Buckfield for the 1942 murder of Mrs Ellen Ann Symes in a road near her home?

37 Since Brian Donald Hume was acquitted of the 1949 murder of second-hand car dealer Stanley Setty how do we know that he was, in fact, guilty of that crime?

> **38** What was the occupation of convicted murderer Frederick Bywaters who, together with his lover, was executed for stabbing a man to death in the street in 1922?

39 In which type of shop was Mrs Elsie May Batten working as an assistant when she was murdered by the twenty-one-year-old Eurasian Edwin Bush in London, in 1961?

40 What was the motive for the murder of Mrs Phoebe Hogg by Mrs Mary Eleanor Pearcey in London in 1890?

41 What was the occupation of Charles Ellsome, subsequently convicted of the 1911 murder of his mistress, Rose Render, in a London street?

42 In which city was the Countess Krystyna Skarbek stabbed to death, in 1952, by Dennis Muldowney?

43 What was the occupation of twenty-seven-year-old Catherine Russell, stabbed to death in a London hotel by Tony Marriott, in 1980?

44 In which publication had some nude and semi-nude photographs of Eve Stratford appeared shortly before she was slashed to death in her East London flat in 1975 by a murderer who has, to date, never been caught?

45 What was the nationality of Francesco Corapi who, in 1986, having stabbed his wife Rosa to death, set fire to their flat, stabbed himself, then leapt to his death from a bedroom window?

46 In which county was the dismembered body of a second-hand car dealer Stanley Setty discovered, in marshes, in 1949?

47 What was the occupation of Rose Muriel Atkins, stabbed to death and left lying in the road by George Brain, in London, in 1938?

48 What was the name of the legendary murderer who in 1885 survived three attempts to execute him at Exeter gaol?

49 In which county in 1980 did thirty-four-year-old Russell John Hart kill Steven and Hilary Burroughs in their home?

50 What was the motive for the 1986 killing of Mrs Paulette Lynn, by her factory worker husband Ken Lynn, which led the court to accept his plea of not guilty to murder but guilty of manslaughter?

51 What was the nickname of murderer Nicky Xinaris who, in 1955, stabbed to death a young soldier outside the 'Blue Kettle' café in Islington, North London?

52 In which county did Richard Dadd stab and slash his father Robert to death, while out walking, in 1843?

53 How many people were convicted of the 1902 murder of twenty-three-year-old Rose Harsent, at her employer's home in Peasenhall, Suffolk?

54 In which county did the 1911 murder of Elizabeth Loake, by her estranged husband George, an then unemployed, take place.

55 How many people were eventually convicted of the famous 'Gorse Hall Murder', involving the stabbing to death of wealthy businessman George Harry Storrs in 1909?

56 In what controversial area of politics was the seventy-eight-year-old spinster Miss Hilda Murrell an active campaigner when she was repeatedly stabbed and left to die at Moat Copse, several miles from her home in Shrewsbury, in 1984?

57 In what type of location did the subsequently convicted murderer Frederick Ballington stab his wife Ann to death, in Manchester, in the summer of 1908?

> **58** In which branch of the armed services, highly relevant to his subsequent disposal of the body of his victim, second-hand car dealer Stanley Setty, had the murderer Brian Donald Hume at one time served?

59 In which county did the sensational 1922 murder case involving Frederick Bywaters and his lover, which resulted in the stabbing to death of a man in the street, take place?

> **60** At the 1951 trial of William Donoghue for the killing of Thomas Meaney, for what reason did the prosecution accept a plea of guilty to manslaughter?

Question Rating (R3)

61 In which part of Britain had the subsequently convicted murderer Richard Prince, who stabbed William Terriss to death in a London street in 1897, been born?

> **62** What old Sikh custom was it suggested that Suchnam Singh Sandhu was attempting to follow in dismembering and subsequently disposing of the parts of his victim's body at Barking, Essex, in 1968?

63 What rank in the armed services was held by Reginald Sidney Buckfield at the time he murdered Mrs Ellen Ann Symes, in a road near her home, in 1942?

64 In which country did the legendary Victorian murderer 'John Lee of Babbacombe' eventually die in 1933?

65 What incident, in 1934, raised doubts about the fact that George Fratson was guilty of the 1928 murder of men's outfitter George Armstrong, in his lock-up shop?

66 For which shipping line did the murderer Frederick Bywaters, who stabbed his lover's husband to death in a suburban London street in 1922, work?

67 What was the nationality of Kate Webster, alias Catherine Lawler, who in 1879 murdered her employer, a Mrs Thomas, at Richmond, Surrey?

68 When Stanley Eric Hobday murdered Charles William Fox, after breaking into his home in West Bromwich, Staffordshire, in 1933, by what novel medium did the police attempt to give the public a description of the man they wished to interview?

69 With what weapon did the killer Ginter Wiora stab to death his girlfriend, Shirley Allen, in her Bayswater flat in 1957?

70 From which terminal disease was the killer William Pettit suffering when he stabbed Mrs Agnes Irene Brown to death in Chislehurst, Kent, in 1953?

71 What was the occupation of Arthur Reginald Baker, stabbed to death in a London street by his lover Kitty Byron in 1902?

72 In which county did the 1986 slaying of sixty-seven-year-old Mrs Bronwen Nixon, a hotel owner, by David Wynne Roberts, take place?

73 When the killer of Mrs Agnes Irene Brown, William Pettit, was eventually located in the City of London in 1953, why was he never charged with her murder?

74 What had been the former occupation of unemployed sixty-four-year-old George Loake, convicted of the 1911 murder of his estranged wife Elizabeth?

75 What was the nationality of Henry Kinch, convicted of the murder and subsequent dismemberment of his landlord at his bedsit in Harlesden in 1968?

76 What occupation was the nineteen-year-old waitress Rose Render following when she was stabbed to death in a London street by her paramour, Charles Ellsome, in 1911?

77 How was James Billington, a neighbour of the Bolton wife-murderer Patrick McKenna, involved with the eventual death of McKenna himself in 1901?

78 What was the name of the woman whose death from a heart attack, while the police were at her North London home, sparked off the 1985 riots which resulted in the stabbing and hacking to death of Keith Blakelock?

79 In which town did the 1964 murder of John Alan West by Peter Anthony Allen and Gwynne Owen Evans take place?

80 How many people were convicted of the 1984 murder of seventy-eight-year-old noted rose grower Hilda Murrell, whose body was found at Moat Copse, several miles away from her home in Shrewsbury?

81 In which London suburb was the body of Rose Muriel Atkins, stabbed to death by George Brain in 1938, found lying in the road by a passing motorist?

82 How did the killer Russell John Hart, who in 1980 had stabbed to death Steven and Hilary Burroughs in their home, eventually come into police custody?

83 In which county did the 1928 murder of George Armstrong, a men's outfitter killed in his lock-up shop by George Fratson, take place?

84 What was the occupation of George Baron Pateman who, in Finchley, London, in 1910 murdered parlour maid Alice Isobel Linfold?

85 Where in London did Albert Edward Marjeram murder Edith May Parker while she was out walking with her sister in 1930?

86 Near what spectacular natural feature did the 1786 murder of an unknown traveller, stabbed to death by his three companions at Hindhead, Surrey, take place?

87 How did her killer David Wynne Roberts come to be staying in the hotel where he stabbed to death the owner, sixty-seven-year-old Mrs Bronwen Nixon, in 1986?

88 Why, in the eighteenth and nineteenth centuries, were suspected murderers, in custody, made to touch the body of their victim prior to charges being brought?

89 To which branch of the armed services did Gunner Matthew Smith, subsequently convicted of the 1944 murder of lorry driver Charles Gilbey at 'Charlie Brown's' public house, in Limehouse, London, belong?

> **90** When, in 1980, Miss Gwendoline Marshall was stabbed and slashed to death in her home in the village of Pluckley, Kent, by Peter Luckhurst, with what was her body pinned by the neck to the floor?

Question Rating (R4)

91 What was the nickname of murderer Reginald Sidney Buckfield who in 1942, in a road near her home, stabbed Mrs Ellen Ann Symes to death?

> **92** In an as yet unsolved 1982 murder case, in what sort of highly illegal activity was the victim Sergio Vaccari believed to be involved when he was stabbed to death in a frenzied attack at his London flat?

93 What was so horrific about the dismemberment of his victim by murderer Suchnam Singh Sandhu in Barking, Essex, in 1968?

> **94** What weapon had Reginald Sidney Buckfield used to murder Mrs Ellen Ann Symes, in a road near her home in 1942?

95 Outside what type of establishment in 1958 was Reginald Summers stabbed to death by Ronald Henry Marwood, during an affray in Holloway, North London?

96 What was the occupation of Georgina Hoffman, stabbed to death in her London flat by Arthur James Mahoney in 1939?

97 What type of establishment did murderer Robert Blakesley burst into and stab his wife and the keeper to death in London in 1841?

98 What were the identical occupations of Peter Anthony Allen and Gywnne Owen Evans, convicted of the 1964 murder of John Alan West at his home in the North of England?

99 In which city, in the North of England, did the killer Francesco Corapi stab to death his wife in 1986, then commit suicide before he could be arrested?

100 In perhaps Surrey's most famous old murder case, what was the occupation of the unidentified man stabbed to death in 1786 by his three companions, at Hindhead near the London-to-Portsmouth road?

101 In which country did the 1949 killing of Squadron Sergeant-Major Williams of the Royal Corps of Signals by his wife of less than three months, Margaret, take place?

102 In which North of England city did the 1925 'gangland' murder of William Plommer, a former boxer, by the Fowler brothers, Lawrence and Wilfred, take place?

103 What nationality was the twenty-year-old chef Georges Castillo, found not guilty by a 1987 Old Bailey jury of the frenzied stabbing to death of his elderly landlady Myra Meyers in her North London flat, but certified as schizophrenic and returned to his own country?

104 In which part of London did the horrific 1980 murder of Donald Ryan, by John Bowden, Michael Ward and David Begley, take place?

105 Of what two types of business was George Harry Storrs, stabbed to death at his Gorse Hall home in 1909, the wealthy owner?

106 In 1983 Mrs Janet Clarke and her brother Philip Huddleston were convicted, at Birmingham Crown Court, following the slaying of her sixty-three-year-old husband Harry Clarke. How long had the Clarkes been married?

107 When Brian Donald Hume was acquitted of the murder of second-hand car dealer Stanley Setty in 1950, for what offence was he sentenced to twelve years' imprisonment?

108 When Frederick Bywaters was charged with the murder of a man he stabbed to death in the street in 1922, what defence did he put forward at his trial?

109 In what capacity was murderer François Benjamin Courvoisier employed by his victim Lord William Russell, whom he killed in his London home in 1840?

110 What was the original nationality of the Countess Krystyna Skarbek, generally known as Christine Granville, who was stabbed to death by Dennis Muldowney in 1952?

111 When Mrs Ellen Ann Symes was stabbed to death by Reginald Sidney Buckfield in 1942 in a road near her home, who was accompanying her, witnessed the attack and escaped without injury?

112 In which country was the murderer Brian Donald Hume, acquitted of the 1949 murder of second-hand car dealer Stanley Setty, eventually sentenced to life imprisonment for the shooting of a taxi driver?

113 What plea did the murderer Arthur James Mahoney enter at his trial in 1939 for the killing of Georgina Hoffman in her London flat in the same year?

114 What was the occupation of the killer Ginter Wiora, convicted of the 1957 slaying of his girlfriend Shirley Allen in her Bayswater flat?

115 When Arthur Thistlewood killed a 'Bow Street Runner' with his sword, during a police raid in Cato Street, London, in 1820, what audacious crime had he and his associates been engaged in planning?

116 Following the 1933 killing of Charles William Fox by Stanley Eric Hobday in West Bromwich, Staffordshire, what extraordinary physical feature possessed by the murderer eventually helped secure his conviction?

117 Which medium was used in 1953 for the first time in the course of a murder inquiry, to locate William Pettit, who had killed Mrs Agnes Irene Brown in the same year, in Chislehurst, Kent?

118 By what first name was Emily Jane Dimmock, found dead with her throat cut at her lodgings in Camden Town, North London, in 1907, known to her friends?

119 In what type of establishment in the Peak District did the 1927 murder of Mrs Amy Collinson, by George Frederick Walter Hayward, take place?

120 What was the occupation of twenty-four-year-old Kitty Byron, convicted of stabbing to death her lover Arthur Reginald Baker in a London street in 1902?

Question Rating (R5)

121 What article of clothing, left at the scene of the crime, led to the arrest and conviction of William Butler for the 1938 murder of a jeweller, Ernest Percival Key, at his shop in Surbiton, Surrey?

122 With what weapon had Brian Donald Hume murdered second-hand car dealer Stanley Setty at his home in 1949?

123 In which county did the 1963 murder, at his farm, of William Garfield Rowe by Russell Pascoe and Dennis Whitty, take place?

124 What was the occupation of Frederick Bywaters' victim, for whose murder both he and his lover were executed in 1923?

125 How did murderer Henry Kinch, who killed and then dismembered the body of his landlord at his bedsit in Harlesden in 1968, first come to the notice of the police in connection with this crime?

126 What had been the wartime occupation of the Countess Krystyna Skarbeck, also known as Christine Granville, stabbed to death by Dennis Muldowney in 1952?

127 With what type of weapon did the killer Tony Marriott stab to death Catherine Russell in a London hotel in 1980?

128 In what type of institution did the 1986 stabbing to death of thirteen-year-old Ahmed Ullah by Darren Coulburn, take place?

129 When Russell Pascoe and Dennis Whitty murdered sixty-four-year-old recluse William Garfield Rowe at his farm in 1963 they failed to discover large sums of money hidden by the victim. In which language had Rowe left directions on how to find them?

130 In what sort of establishment had the stabbing to death of newsagent Billy Osu by Dennis Kelly, convicted of this crime in 1983, taken place?

131 What was the occupation of John Alan West, found dead with a stab wound in the chest and severe head injuries, of whose 1964 murder Peter Anthony Allen and Gwynne Owen Evans were subsequently found guilty?

132 When Leonard Jack Thomas was brought to trial at the Old Bailey in 1949, on a charge of murdering his wife Florence in the same year, what, curiously, was the offence for which he was already serving seven years' imprisonment?

133 What was the self-confessed motive for Albert Edward Marjeram's murder of Edith May Parker while she was out walking with her sister in London in 1930?

134 With what everyday article did George Baron Pateman murder parlour maid Alice Isobel Linfold in Finchley, London, in 1910?

135 What was the occupation of Elliot Bower who, in a sensational Victorian murder scandal, stabbed to death his wife's lover Saville Morton in London in 1852?

136 In which North of England city had the stabbing to death of newsagent Billy Osu taken place resulting in the 1983 conviction of Dennis Kelly?

137 What highly identifiable item taken from victim John Alan West was found in the possession of Gwynne Owen Evans and helped lead to his conviction together with Peter Anthony Allen, for this 1964 murder?

138 Why, in 1986, had the unemployed domestic assistant, Francesco Corapi stabbed his wife to death then taken his own life before he could be convicted of her murder?

139 What was the occupation of Leonard Jack Thomas who in London in 1949 stabbed his wife Florence to death?

140 In what type of vehicle did driver George Brain transport his victim Rose Muriel Atkins before and after he murdered her in London in 1938?

141 What was the occupation of Ronald Henry Marwood, convicted of the 1958 murder of Raymond Summers in the street at Holloway, North London?

142 What was the exotic occupation of Eve Stratford, slashed to death in her East London flat in March 1975 by a murderer who, to date, has never been caught?

143 In what sort of location was Mrs Carol Martin, a thirty-eight-year-old mother of two young children, stabbed to death by twenty-year-old Stuart Hopkins in Redditch, Worcestershire, in 1986?

144 Why did thirty-eight-year-old Valerie Flood stab her husband Maurice to death on Christmas Eve 1985, in their Walworth home – a crime for which she was placed on probation for three years after pleading not guilty to murder, but guilty to manslaughter?

145 In which county did the 1986 killing of Mrs Paulette Lynn by her factory worker husband Ken Lynn, take place?

146 In the celebrated 1862 slaying of servant girl Jessie McPherson by Jessie M'Lachlan, a former servant in the same household, what weapon had the murderer used?

147 What was the apparent motive for the 1901 murder of Mrs Anna McKenna by her husband Patrick, in Bolton, Lancashire?

148 In which county did the 1908 slaying of Boer War widow Thirza Isabella Kelly by seventeen-year-old John Edward Casey, who some two years previously had cut up a pig, dressed it in female underclothes and left it in his parents' sitting room, take place?

149 What was the occupation of Arthur James Mahoney, convicted of the 1939 murder of Georgina Hoffman in her London flat?

150 Russell Pascoe and Dennis Whitty murdered sixty-four-year-old recluse, William Garfield Rowe, at his farm in 1963. Why had Rowe been living in secrecy for thirty-nine years?

CHAPTER SIX

MULTIPLE MURDERERS

Question Rating (R1)

1 How had each of the victims of the undetected murderer, known as 'Jack the Ripper', been slain in the East End of London in 1888, prior to the mutilation of their bodies?

2 What was the nickname given to the multiple murderer Peter Sutcliffe who between 1975 and 1980 terrorized women throughout Lancashire, Yorkshire and Greater Manchester?

3 By what infamous nickname was the robber, kidnapper and multiple murderer Donald Neilson, known in the popular press in the mid 1970s?

4 In 1888 what occupation did all the victims of the undetected murderer, known as 'Jack the Ripper', have in common?

5 In which sport did the infamous Kray twins turn professional at the age of seventeen?

6 What was the name of the seventeen-year-old girl kidnapped, held to ransom and then murdered by Donald Neilson in 1975?

7 What method of killing his female victims did the multiple murderer George Joseph Smith, executed in 1915, regularly employ?

   8 By what nickname was the murderer John George Haigh known to the public, because of his method of disposing of the corpses of his victims?

9 How many police officers were murdered by Harry Maurice Roberts and his associates in 1966 in a street in Hammersmith, West London?

   10 What were the first names of the three Kray brothers, two of whom were tried at the Old Bailey in 1969 for murder?

11 What was the occupation of the multiple killer Dennis Andrew Nilsen when arrested and tried in 1983 for the murder of over a dozen victims?

   12 How many people were eventually convicted, at the Old Bailey, of the 1966 murders of a number of police officers in a street in Hammersmith, West London?

13 What was the name given, because of his method of killing, to the multiple murderer George Joseph Smith who between 1912 and 1914 was responsible for the deaths of three women?

   14 How many times did the undetected murderer, known as 'Jack the Ripper', carry out a 'double murder' in the East End of London in 1888?

15 What was the name of the notorious South London gang whose feud with the Kray twins, for control of London's underworld, raged throughout the 1960s?

16 How many victims did the undetected murderer, known as 'Jack the Ripper', slay in London's East End between August and November 1888?

17 Which famous counsel unsuccessfully defended the multiple killer George Joseph Smith at his trial for murder in 1915?

18 What was different from his other killings in 1888 in the murder and mutilation of Mary Jane Kelly, the final victim of the undetected murderer known as 'Jack the Ripper'?

19 For what reason did the robber, kidnapper and multiple murderer Donald Neilson acquire his infamous nickname in the mid 1970s?

20 How many victims is it believed that the multiple murderer George Joseph Smith killed between 1912 and 1914?

21 In which county did the 1952 murder of Charles Henry Giffard and his wife, by their son Miles Giffard, take place?

22 What revolting ritual did the murderer John George Haigh claim to have carried out on each of his victims prior to disposing of their bodies?

23 Which member of the Royal Family was, at one time, suspected of being the infamous murderer known as 'Jack the Ripper' who in 1888 terrorized London's East End?

24 What did most, but not all, of the female victims attacked by the multiple murderer Peter Sutcliffe between 1975 and 1980, have in common?

25 A tape recording, allegedly sent by the multiple murderer Peter Sutcliffe to investigating officers, had a very strong regional accent. Which accent?

26 Which of the infamous Kray twins is a self-confessed bisexual?

27 How were most of the multiple murderer Dennis Andrew Nilsen's victims killed before he dismembered them?

28 Near which prison, in London, did the 1966 murders of a number of police officers by Harry Maurice Roberts and his associates take place?

29 What gruesome item, sent in a cardboard box to the chairman of a Vigilance Committee in the East End of London in 1888, purported to have come from the undetected murderer, known as 'Jack the Ripper'?

30 All but one of the victims of the undetected murderer, known as 'Jack the Ripper', murdered in London's East End in 1888, were killed within the jurisdiction of the Metropolitan Police Force. In which police area was the other one killed?

Question Rating (R2)

31 What was the profession of Olive Balchin, murdered in 1946 by Walter Graham Rowland?

32 In which city did the 1913 execution of Patrick Higgins for the murder of his two young sons in 1911 take place?

33 What was noticeable about the stature of the notorious Victorian 'cat-burglar' and murderer Charles Frederick Peace?

34 In which town in Kent did the 1975 murder of a Catholic priest by Patrick Mackay, a twenty-two-year-old pyschopath and subsequently convicted multiple murderer, take place?

35 What occupation did the three men, shot dead by robber and subsequently convicted multiple murderer Donald Neilson in the mid 1970s, have in common?

36 What did all the female victims of the murderer George Joseph Smith have in common when they met their deaths, between 1912 and 1914?

37 What was the name of the notorious Victorian criminal eventually executed at Armley Gaol, Leeds, in 1879, for the 1876 murder by shooting of Arthur Dyson in Sheffield, Yorkshire?

38 In what specific medium did the murderer John George Haigh attempt to destroy the corpses of his victims?

39 Of how many murders was Peter Thomas Anthony Manuel convicted at his trial in Glasgow in 1958?

40 How did Gordon Frederick Cummins murder all of his female victims?

41 What profession did both Norah Upchurch and Beatrice Sutton, the victims of Frederick Herbert Charles Field, have in common?

42 What was the nickname of Annie Chapman, the second victim of 'Jack the Ripper', who was killed and mutilated in the East End of London in 1888?

43 With which type of weapon did Peter Thomas Anthony Manuel carry out two triple murders, of the families whose houses he was burgling, in Scotland in 1956 and 1958?

44 From which branch of the armed services had the murderer Frederick Herbert Charles Field earlier deserted, resulting in his initial arrest?

45 How were all the police officers, murdered by Harry Maurice Roberts and his associates in 1966 in a West London street, actually killed by their assailants?

46 What was the name of the multiple murderer Peter Sutcliffe's foreign-born wife?

47 From which country was the fugitive killer Ian Wood eventually extradited to face trial in Britain for the murder of his lover, Mrs Danielle Lloyd, and her daughter, Stephanie, at his country mansion in 1986?

48 How was the small-time villain George Cornell murdered by Ronald Kray in an East End public house in 1966?

49 Where in Britain was the multiple murderer Dennis Andrew Nilsen born in November 1945?

50 What was the name of the so-called 'Mad Axe Man' whom the Kray twins helped to escape from Dartmoor Prison then hid, but who was never seen nor heard of again after Christmas 1966?

51 Why is it unsurprising that all of Dennis Andrew Nilsen's victims were young men and none were female?

52 What was the nickname of Jack McVitie, the small-time crook murdered by Reginald Kray in a North London flat in 1967?

53 To which branch of the armed services did the wartime murderer Gordon Frederick Cummins belong?

54 In what type of wartime location was the body of Olive Balchin, murdered by Walter Graham Rowland in 1946, found a few hours after the crime?

55 What was the occupation of the multiple murderer, Peter Sutcliffe who, between 1975 and 1980, terrorized women throughout the Lancashire, Yorkshire and Greater Manchester areas?

56 What was the first name of Mrs Kray, the influential mother of the infamous Kray twins?

57 What highly incriminating item, which eventually led to his arrest, did the multiple murderer Gordon Frederick Cummins leave in the street, after unsuccessfully attempting to murder yet another woman?

58 How was the small-time crook, Jack McVitie, murdered by Reginald Kray in a North London flat in 1967?

59 By what name did the notorious East End gang, headed by the Kray twins, come to be known in the 1960s?

60 Which famous public school had the murderer Miles Giffard, who battered his parents to death in 1952, once attended?

Question Rating (R3)

61 Following his conviction for the 1946 murder of Olive Balchin, what incident threw doubt upon the correctness of the verdict in the case of Walter Graham Rowland?

> **62** What was the name of the legendary Scotland Yard detective who led the hunt for the culprits, following the murder of George Cornell in London's East End in 1966?

63 In what type of location, in 1953, were the bodies of John and Phoebe Harries found, buried in the ground, after they had been battered to death by their adopted nephew Thomas Ronald Lewis Harries?

> **64** Where, specifically, were the Kray twins, when they were finally arrested in May 1968 at a flat in Shoreditch?

65 In which city had the body of Olive Balchin been discovered in 1946, following her murder by Walter Graham Rowland a few hours previously?

> **66** On which infamous historical figure did the psychopathic multiple murderer Patrick Mackay, sentenced to life imprisonment in 1975, model himself and identify with?

67 In which country had the wife of the multiple murderer Peter Sutcliffe been born?

> **68** After murdering his wife Greeta Healey and stepdaughter Marie Walker at their home in Stockport, Cheshire, in 1986, where did Robert Healey bury their bodies in a shallow grave?

69 In which county did the 1986 murders of Mrs Danielle Lloyd (née Ledez) and her daughter Stephanie by Danielle's lover Ian Wood take place?

70 What was the occupation of the infamous kidnapper, robber and murderer Donald Neilson, who operated in the mid 1970s in the Midlands and North of England?

71 In which country was the multiple murderer and confidence trickster Frederick Bayley Deeming eventually hanged in 1892?

72 In 1931 and again in 1936, Frederick Herbert Charles Field murdered a female victim. On both occasions what incident, of his own making, led to his being tried for murder?

73 In which city in the North-East of England in 1915, 1925 and 1939 did William Burkitt kill his current mistress, on each occasion being charged with murder but convicted of manslaughter?

74 With how many murders was the multiple killer George Joseph Smith charged at his trial in 1915?

75 How did the murderer John George Haigh kill his victim Mrs Olive Durand-Deacon at his Sussex 'factory', prior to attempting to dispose of her body?

76 In what type of location was fugitive Harry Maurice Roberts, concerned in the murders of a number of police officers in a West London street in 1966, eventually found hiding?

77 In which regiment of the British Army did the Kray twins briefly serve during their National Service?

78 How did Ian Wood kill his lover, Mrs Danielle Lloyd (née Ledez) and her daughter Stephanie, at his country mansion in 1986?

79 Walter Dew, the young detective called to investigate the death of Mary Jane Kelly, the last victim of the undetected murderer known as 'Jack the Ripper' later gained fame as the man who arrested whch other murderer?

80 When thirty-seven-year-old Ian Wood killed his lover, Mrs Danielle Lloyd and her daughter Stephanie, what agreement did he say he had made with her prior to her death?

81 What was the nickname of Elizabeth Stride, the third victim of the undetected murderer known as 'Jack the Ripper' who was killed and multilated in the East End of London in 1888?

82 In which part of the country did the 1953 murders of John and Phoebe Harries by their adopted nephew, Thomas Ronald Lewis Harries, take place?

83 How had the murderer Walter Graham Rowland savagely killed his victim, Olive Balchin, in 1946?

84 In which city did Scotland's then longest multiple murder trial take place in 1984?

85 What was the occupation of Ian Wood who murdered his lover, Mrs Danielle Lloyd and her daughter Stephanie, at his country mansion in 1986?

86 With how many murders was the infamous kidnapper and robber, Donald Neilson, charged at his trial in Oxford in 1976?

87 In which part of London was the murderer George Joseph Smith born in 1872?

88 What had been the occupation of Nicholas Cock, shot dead by the notorious Victorian criminal Charles Frederick Peace in 1876?

89 In which county had the multiple murderer John George Haigh, executed in 1949 for the murder of Mrs Olive Durand-Deacon, been born?

90 What, ironically, was the occupation of Charles Henry Giffard who, together with his wife, was battered to death by their son Miles Giffard in 1952?

Question Rating (R4)

91 Because of his willingness to help the police with their inquiries, what nickname did the multiple murder Peter Thomas Anthony Manuel earn for himself?

92 In what type of vehicle were Harry Maurice Roberts and his associates travelling when stopped by police officers in a West London street in 1966, which action led to the deaths of those officers?

93 How were six members of the extended Doyle family murdered in a Glasgow council flat in 1984?

94 In which county did the 1940 murder of three women, in the grounds of a cottage at Matfield, take place?

95 How was the partially dismembered torso of small-time crook William Henry Moseley, lacking both head and hands, positively identified following a post-mortem examination in 1975?

96 Which one of the men convicted in 1966 of murder in a case involving a number of police officers in a West London street, died in Parkhurst Prison, Isle of Wight, in 1981?

97 What was the nickname given, because of its virtual impregnability, to the 1960s family home of the Kray twins, in Vallance Road, East London?

98 With how many murders was Dennis Andrew Nilsen charged when he appeared for trial at the Old Bailey in October 1983?

99 Which everyday tool, eventually found on his arrest, had Peter Sutcliffe used to batter a number of his victims to death prior to mutilating their bodies?

100 Walter Graham Rowland, who was executed in 1947 for the 1946 murder of Olive Balchin, had already occupied the death cell at Strangeways Prison following his murder of a member of his family in 1934. Which member?

101 Of how many killings, between 1975 and 1980, was the multiple murderer Peter Sutcliffe convicted at his Old Bailey trial in 1981?

102 In which county in 1982 were two women, Mrs Margaret Johnson and Mrs Ann Lee, savagely killed, while out walking their dogs, by the subsequently convicted murderer Peter Fell?

103 Following what incident in 1984 at Wormwood Scrubs Prison, was the multiple murderer Dennis Andrew Nilsen transferred to Parkhurst Prison, Isle of Wight?

104 What type of car did the murderer John George Haigh own, in which he drove Mrs Olive Durand-Deacon to her death at his 'factory' in Sussex in 1949?

105 What political affiliations did the multiple killer Dennis Andrew Nilsen espouse during his spate of murders between 1978 and 1983?

106 How did the multiple murderer Peter Sutcliffe come, eventually, to be arrested in January 1981?

107 In which British city, near the scene of one of his crimes, was the multiple murderer and confidence trickster Frederick Bayley Deeming born around 1840?

108 What was the occupation of William Burkitt, who in 1915, 1925 and 1939 killed his mistresses, and on each occasion, having been charged with murder, was convicted of manslaughter?

109 How had the three women murdered in the grounds of a cottage at Matfield in 1940 all been killed?

110 With what household implement did Robert Healey batter his wife Greeta to death, at their home in Stockport, Cheshire, in 1986?

111 How did the murderer Peter Fell savagely kill Mrs Margaret Johnson and Mrs Ann Lee, both of whom were out walking their dogs, in 1982?

112 How did the notorious kidnapper, robber and murderer Donald Neilson eventually come to be arrested in December 1975 in Nottinghamshire?

113 Where were the bodies of Charles Henry Giffard and his wife, battered to death by their son Miles Giffard, eventually discovered by the police?

114 What had been the classic motive for Charles Frederick Peace's shooting dead of Arthur Dyson in Sheffield, Yorkshire, in 1876?

115 For the murders of how many women was Gordon Frederick Cummins tried at the Old Bailey in 1942?

116 What was the name of the drinking club, opened in London's Bow Road by Reginald Kray, whose title was meant to honour himself and his brother, Ronald?

117 How, in 1915, 1925 and 1939, did William Burkitt kill his current mistress, each time being charged with murder but convicted of manslaughter?

118 What was the phonetic call sign of the police 'Q' car in which the officers, murdered in 1966 by Harry Maurice Roberts and his associates, were travelling?

119 How did the detectives investigating the 1953 murders of John and Phoebe Harries get the suspect, their adopted nephew Thomas Ronald Lewis Harries, to give away where he had buried their bodies?

120 What was the name of the Metropolitan Police Commissioner, nominally in charge of the hunt in 1888 for the undetected murderer, known as 'Jack the Ripper', in London's East End?

Question Rating (R5)

121 What happened to Reginald Kray's twenty-three-year-old wife, Frances, after less than two years of marriage to the infamous gangster?

122 What was the original name of the infamous killer, Donald Neilson, convicted on several counts of murder, for each of which he received a sentence of life imprisonment?

123 In which regiment of the British Army had George Joseph Smith served for two years, in the 1890s, before beginning his murderous exploits?

124 When John George Haigh induced Mrs Olive Durand-Deacon to accompany him to his 'factory' in Sussex in 1949 with the intention of killing her and disposing of her body, what business venture had they ostensibly gone there to discuss?

125 Rivalry concerning what type of business enterprise led to the deaths of several members of the extended Doyle family in a council flat, in Glasgow, in 1984?

126 To which devout religious group did the parents of the multiple murderer, John George Haigh, belong?

127 What were the names of the police officers, murdered in a street in West London in 1966 by Harry Maurice Roberts and his associates?

128 How many murders, in all, did John George Haigh confess to, prior to his 1949 trial for the murder of Mrs Olive Durand-Deacon at Lewes Assize Court?

129 In what type of conveyance did the murderer Miles Giffard move the bodies of his mother and father from their house to their place of concealment after he had battered them to death in 1952?

130 What were the surnames of Harry Maurice Roberts' associates in the 1966 slaying of a number of police officers in a West London street?

131 With what household implement did Gordon Frederick Cummins mutilate the dead body of his second victim, Evelyn Oatley, in 1942, thereby evoking comparisons with the 'Jack the Ripper' murders?

132 Following the conviction, in 1977, of Reginald Dudley and Robert Maynard for the murders of William Henry Moseley and his close friend Michael Henry Cornwall, where in Islington was Moseley's skull found 'thawing out'?

133 From which country did the name 'Kray', borne by two of London's most infamous convicted murderers Ronald and Reginald, originate?

134 How many victims is the multiple murderer Dennis Andrew Nilsen *known* to have killed between 1978 and 1983?

135 What was the name of the West End gaming club opened by the Kray twins in the late 1960s in Wilton Place, Belgravia?

136 In which county in 1956 did the double murders of Mrs Lydia Leakey and her fourteen-year-old daughter Norma, by Albert William Goozee, take place?

137 For what motive was it believed that Walter Graham Rowland savagely murdered Olive Balchin in 1946?

    138 How did murderer Albert William Goozee savagely kill his lover Mrs Lydia Leakey and her fourteen-year-old daughter Norma in 1956?

139 How had Walter Graham Rowland, executed in 1947 for the murder of Olive Balchin, previously killed a member of his family in 1934, for which crime he was sentenced to life imprisonment?

    140 When Peter Fell became a suspect in the 1982 murders of Mrs Margaret Johnson and Mrs Ann Lee, both of whom had been killed while out walking their dogs, the police received thirteen telephone calls between then and his arrest in 1983 stating that he was the murderer. One person had made all these calls. Who?

141 In what type of location did murderer Albert William Goozee savagely slay his lover Mrs Lydia Leakey and her fourteen-year-old daughter Norma in 1956?

    142 In 1891, just prior to fleeing the country, the Victorian confidence trickster and multiple murderer Frederick Bayley Deeming disposed of a number of members of his family, burying them under the floor of a villa in the North of England. Which members of his family?

143 What was the country of origin of Mrs Danielle Lloyd (née Ledez) who, together with her daughter Stephanie, was murdered by Danielle's lover, Ian Wood, at his country mansion in 1986?

144 What was the occupation of Robert Healey who, in 1986, murdered his wife Greeta and stepdaughter Marie Walker at their home in Stockport, Cheshire?

145 From which regiment of the British Army had Peter Fell been medically discharged just two months prior to his savage murder of Mrs Margaret Johnson and Mrs Ann Lee, who were out walking their dogs, in 1982?

146 How many women had Gordon Frederick Cummins murdered before his trial and execution in 1942?

147 Following the deaths of his wife Greeta and stepdaughter Marie Walker, at their home in Stockport, Cheshire, in 1986, by what classic method did their fugitive murderer, Robert Healey, attempt to throw the police off his trail?

148 For how many murders did Dennis Andrew Nilsen admit responsibility when he was arrested by the police in 1983?

149 At his trial in 1956 in Winchester, Albert William Goozee said that his lover Mrs Lydia Leakey and her fourteen-year-old daughter Norma had killed each other in a fight, after first attacking him. Why was he not believed?

150 What was the occupation of Walter Graham Rowland, subsequently convicted of the 1946 murder of Olive Balchin?

CHAPTER SEVEN

CHILD AND
SEX MURDERERS

Question Rating (R1)

1 What were the names of the two infamous murderers convicted in 1966 of the so-called 'Moors Murders'?

> **2** What was the occupation of Beverley Allitt who was convicted of the 1991 murders of several children at Nottingham Crown Court in 1993?

3 By what, then innovative, investigative technique was the murderer Colin Pitchfork identified as the killer of two schoolgirls in Leicestershire and brought to justice in 1987?

> **4** How, between 1963 and 1965, were the child victims of the 'Moors Murderers' actually killed?

5 How did the infamous Victorian murderess, Amelia Elizabeth Dyer, make her living?

> **6** From what sexual perversion did the convicted murderer John Reginald Halliday Christie suffer?

7 In which city in 1968 did Mary Flora Bell, kill two boys, aged three and four years?

8 In 1966 two infamous murderers were sent to prison for life for the so-called 'Moors Murders'; to which North of England moors does this epithet refer?

9 Which famous actor portrayed a notorious multiple sex murderer in the film *10 Rillington Place*?

10 Which sadistic sex killer was responsible for the brutal murders of Mrs Margery Gardner and Miss Doreen Marshall, within two weeks of each other, in 1946?

11 How did Thomas Henry Allaway murder his victim Irene Wilkins in 1921, after luring her to the South Coast in her search for a job?

12 Which member of the House of Lords has shown a keen interest in the case of the convicted murderess Myra Hindley, imprisoned for life in 1966 for the murder of a child?

13 When the child killer John Thomas Straffen murdered his final victim, from which location (to which he had been sent in 1951) was he on the run?

14 In which city was the infamous child murderer Ian Brady born in 1938?

15 Who was eventually convicted of the killing of six prostitutes in the Hammersmith area of London between 1964 and 1965, which crimes came to be known as the 'Hammersmith nude murders'?

16 What nationality was the infamous killer of the 1950s, Patrick Joseph Byrne?

17 What was the name of the homosexual male prostitute strangled in a house in Catford, London, in 1972, which case led to the conviction of three defendants (later exonerated and released by the Court of Appeal)?

18 In which city did both the murderer Derrick Edwardson and his victim, four-year-old Edwina Taylor, live at the time of his offence in 1957?

19 What gruesome discovery, hidden in a tobacco box, was made by the police when searching the London home of John Reginald Halliday Christie in 1953?

20 By what sort of firm were Ian Brady and Myra Hindley both employed at the time they first met in 1961, prior to their murderous spate of child killings?

21 How did the murderer and sexual psychopath John Reginald Halliday Christie render his victims unconscious prior to strangling them in his own home?

22 What had been the wartime occupation of the subsequently convicted murderer John Reginald Halliday Christie?

23 How old was Mary Flora Bell when, in 1968, she was found guilty, on the grounds of diminished responsibility, of the manslaughter of two boys aged three and four years?

24 In which part of Britain were the schoolgirls Freda Burnell and Florence Irene Little killed by murderer Harold Jones in 1921?

25 In which town, in 1953, did the killing of six-year-old Mary Hackett by the subsequently convicted murderer George Albert Hall take place?

26 In a suburb of which city was the infamous child murderer Myra Hindley born in 1942?

27 By what name was the multiple killer Kenneth Erskine, who was active in South London during 1986, known in the press?

28 The multiple murderer John Francis Duffy was the first man in English criminal history to be identified by what investigative procedure?

29 What type of victims, in the main, did the multiple killer Michael Lupo murder during his spate of killings in London, in 1986?

30 What job was thirteen-year-old Carl Bridgewater engaged on when he was murdered after disturbing a gang of robbers, in a sensational 1978 case?

Question Rating (R2)

31 In the air force of which allied country did the subsequently convicted murderer Neville George Clevely Heath gain a commission in 1941, prior to his secondment to the Royal Air Force in 1944?

32 How was three-year-old Brian Howe, the second victim of Mary Flora Bell, actually killed by her in 1968?

33 What political sentiments were freely espoused by the multiple child murderer Ian Brady?

34 By what nickname was the killer John Francis Duffy known to the public because of his habit of choosing his victims from close to a certain type of location?

35 How was the thirteen-year-old schoolboy Carl Bridgewater, murdered by a gang of robbers he had disturbed in 1978, actually killed?

36 What nickname, derived from the meaning of his real name, was given to the multiple killer Michael Lupo, arrested for a series of murders in London in 1986?

37 What was the occupation of Thomas Henry Allaway, convicted of the 1921 murder of Irene Wilkins, who was lured to the South Coast by a telegram sent in reply to her advertisement for a job?

38 In what type of location were the bodies of Albert Edward Burrows' four victims all eventually discovered in 1923?

39 How, in 1965, was the child murderer Ian Brady's last victim, a seventeen-year-old homosexual youth called Edward Evans, actually killed?

40 When, just before his execution in 1946, the charming but sadistic murderer Neville George Clevely Heath was granted his last wish by the prison governor, for a whisky, what was he reputed to have said?

41 With what type of weapon did the subsequently convicted murderer Alfred Charles Whiteway kill his two teenage victims, Barbara Songhurst and Christine Reed, near the River Thames at Richmond in 1953?

42 In which branch of the armed services were both the murderer Arthur Heys and his victim Winifred Evans serving when he killed her in 1944?

43 How old was the killer Harold Jones when convicted of the 1921 murder of eleven-year-old Florence Irene Little?

44 How were the two girls, Doreen Hearne, aged eight, and Kathleen Trendle, aged six, actually killed by their murderer Harold Hill, in 1941?

45 Where was murderer John Reginald Halliday Christie born in 1898?

46 At her trial, for the 1899 murder of a child in London, to whom did the murderess Louise Massett say she had entrusted the infant's safekeeping?

47 When Nicholas Price was sentenced to life imprisonment at the Old Bailey in 1985 for his part in the death of three-year-old Heidi Koseda, how had the little girl actually come to die?

48 What was the occupation of the killer George Albert Hall, convicted in 1954 of the murder of six-year-old Mary Hackett?

49 How, in 1968, was eight-year-old Christopher Sabey actually killed by his subsequently convicted murderer Richard Nilsson?

50 What instrument, later found in the personal effects of the murderer Neville George Clevely Heath, had not only inflicted pain but had left incriminatingly distinctive marks on the body of his first victim, found in a London hotel room?

51 What particular type of victims did the multiple murderer Kenneth Erskine attack during his 1986 reign of violence?

52 When the body of eight-year-old Helen Priestley was discovered following her murder by Mrs Jeannie Donald in Scotland in 1934, certain injuries on the body were alleged, at her trial, to have been made by the defendant to make the case appear to be one of what?

53 In which country had the subsequently convicted murderer Michael Lupo been born?

54 What relation was murderer Ronald Barton to his fourteen-year-old victim Keighley Barton, whom he stabbed to death in London in 1985?

55 What was the popular name given to the 1960 and 1961 killings of William Arthur Elliott and George Gerald Stobbs, both killed in a similar fashion in the same location in Chesterfield, Derbyshire, by murderer Michael Copeland?

56 What occupation was shared by Mrs Heather Arnold, subsequently convicted of murdering Mrs Jeanne Sutcliffe and her eight-month-old baby Heidi, at their home in April 1986, and the victims' husband and father Mr Paul Sutcliffe?

57 What were the loathsome 'occupations' of Mrs Annie Walters and Mrs Amelia Sachs both executed in 1903 for the murder, by poisoning, of a child in London?

58 In the sensational 1978 case involving the murder of thirteen-year-old Carl Bridgewater, who had disturbed a gang of robbers at work, how many men were eventually convicted of either murder or manslaughter?

59 How did twenty-three-year-old Peter Griffiths brutally murder three-year-old June Anne Devaney near Blackburn, Lancashire, in 1948?

60 When the London home of John Reginald Halliday Christie was searched by the police in 1953, the remains of how many female bodies were discovered there?

Question Rating (R3)

61 At the outbreak of the Second World War, in which unit of the Army did the subsequently convicted murderer Neville George Clevely Heath enlist?

62 What highly embarrassing and irregular event, as far as the police were concerned, occurred in relation to the murder weapon used by Alfred Charles Whiteway to kill two teenage girls, near the River Thames at Richmond in 1953?

63 In which county did the brutal 1944 murder of Winifred Evans by serviceman Arthur Heys take place?

64 How many children did the subsequently convicted murderer Harold Jones admit to killing, at his trial in 1921?

65 In which county did the 1941 murder of two young girls, Doreen Hearne and Kathleen Trendle, by the serving soldier Harold Hill take place?

66 At what sort of public location was the body of Louise Masset's victim found in London in 1899?

67 How were all of John Thomas Straffen's child victims actually killed by him in the early 1950s?

68 In which county did the 1968 murder of eight-year-old Christopher Sabey, by Richard Nilsson, take place?

69 How did murderess Susan Newell actually kill her thirteen-year-old victim, John Johnston, when he called at her house in Coatbridge, Scotland, in 1923?

70 How many children, is it believed, were murdered by Ian Brady and Myra Hindley between 1963 and 1965?

71 How did Ted Donald Garlick actually kill his victim Carol Ann White in Hayes, Middlesex, in 1962?

72 At his 1988 trial at the Central Criminal Court of how many murders was the killer Kenneth Erskine convicted?

73 What was Ronald Barton's motive in murdering his fourteen-year-old victim Keighley Barton in London in 1985?

74 What relation was Constance Kent to Francis Savill Kent, whom she murdered in the family home in 1860?

75 With the murders of how many people were Ian Brady and Myra Hindley charged at their trial at Chester Assizes in 1966?

76 What did the two victims William Arthur Elliott and George Gerald Stobbs, murdered in 1960 and 1961 respectively in the same location in Chesterfield, Derbyshire, by Michael Copeland, have in common?

77 What was notable about the three telegrams sent by Thomas Henry Allaway in an attempt to lure female victims to the South Coast, one of which resulted in his murdering Irene Wilkins in 1921?

> **78** With what type of weapon did Mrs Heather Arnold, a family friend, murder Mrs Jeanne Sutcliffe and her eight-month-old baby, Heidi, at their home in April 1986?

79 During the investigation into the murder of three-year-old June Anne Devaney, by twenty-two-year-old Peter Griffiths, near Blackburn, Lancashire, in 1948, what massive and unprecedented step did the investigating officers take in apprehending the culprit?

> **80** In which county did twenty-year-old Gary Taken murder nineteen-year-old Tessa Howden in her own home in 1986?

81 What was the name of the ten-year-old girl abducted and murdered in 1964 by Ian Brady and Myra Hindley, whose final moments had been recorded by them on a tape which was subsequently recovered and played at their trial?

> **82** What was the occupation of forty-four-year-old Colin James Evans who, following an indecent assault, killed four-year-old Marie Payne in Epping Forest in 1983?

83 What was the occupation of the multiple child murderess Myra Hindley, sentenced to life imprisonment in 1966?

> **84** What was the murderer Gordon Frederick Cummins training to be when he committed his series of crimes in 1942?

85 What was the occupation of the multiple child murderer Ian Brady, sentenced to life imprisonment in 1966?

86 What unusual motive did murderess Mrs Mincha Beechook claim, at her trial, had driven her to kill four-year-old Stacey Kavanagh and her own seven-year-old daughter Tina, on the same day in London in 1985?

87 What was the unflattering nickname given to murderer and sexual psychopath John Reginald Halliday Christie in his youth, which was to prove a portent of things to come?

88 In which county did Albert Edward Burrows murder his mistress and two children in 1920, and a four-year-old boy in 1923?

89 By what simple, yet ingenious, means did the murderer Neville George Clevely Heath return to his Bournemouth hotel room without being seen, following the horrific murder and mutilation of his second victim in 1946?

90 While on remand in Norwich Prison awaiting his trial for the 1944 murder of Winifred Evans, what, eventually damning, piece of evidence concerning serviceman Arthur Heys came to the notice of his commanding officer?

Question Rating (R4)

91 What improbable name, borrowed in part from a dead poet, did the murderer Neville George Clevely Heath assume, following his flight from London to the South Coast in 1946?

92 What rarely used defence did twenty-seven-year-old Simon Fraser raise at his trial in Edinburgh for the bizarre murder of his eighteen-month-old son, Simon, in their Glasgow home in 1878?

93 How was Winifred Evans actually killed by Arthur Heys, during a brutal sex attack in 1944?

94 In which regiment of the British Army was the killer Michael Douglas Dowdall serving when he battered to death the prostitute Veronica Murray at her home in Kilburn, London, in 1958?

95 What was the occupation of Alfred Charles Whiteway who in 1953 murdered two teenage girls, Barbara Songhurst and Christine Reed, near the River Thames at Richmond?

96 To what did the infamous convicted murderess Myra Hindley confess, while in prison in 1986?

97 In which town in Southern England was the murderer Neville George Clevely Heath born in 1917?

98 For approximately how long was the convicted child strangler John Edward Allen on the run from Broadmoor Criminal Lunatic Asylum, before his recapture in 1949?

99 What was the name of the girl who, together with Mary Flora Bell, was charged with the murders of two boys, aged three and four years, in 1968, but who was acquitted of the charges?

100 In what type of business did Harold Jones, later convicted of killing a number of children in 1921, work as an assistant?

101 In which regiment of the British Army was murderer Harold Hill serving when he killed two young girls, Doreen Hearne and Kathleen Trendle, in 1941?

102 Where did murderer John Reginald Halliday Christie receive injuries as a young man, which resulted in his going blind for a number of months?

103 How had Louise Masset's child victim, found murdered in London in 1899, actually been killed?

104 In what sort of trade was the widower Patrick Higgins, subsequently convicted of the 1911 murders of his two small sons in West Lothian, Scotland, employed?

105 From which institution was the child murderess Beverley Allitt brought to be sentenced to life imprisonment, in 1993?

106 In the investigation into the 1968 killing of eight-year-old Christopher Sabey by Richard Nilsson, samples of what, found on the clothing of both individuals and analysed by the new method of 'neutron activation', helped point to the suspect?

107 When Susan Newell killed her thirteen-year-old victim, John Johnston, at her home in Coatbridge, Scotland, in 1923, what reason had he to be at the house?

108 What was the occupation of thirty-six-year-old Louise Masset, convicted of the murder of a three-year-old infant in London in 1899?

109 Under what circumstances had Ted Donald Garlick, convicted of the 1962 slaying of Carol Ann White, been acquitted some time before of the murder of his wife?

110 What was the name of Myra Hindley's brother-in-law who witnessed the 1965 murder of Edward Evans by Ian Brady and subsequently informed the police?

111 With what type of weapon were the eight-month-old baby and the thirteen-year-old servant of the Marr family bludgeoned to death, at their home in the Ratcliffe Highway, London, by John Williams in December 1811?

112 In which county did the 1919 death of thirteen-year-old Ivy Lydia Wood, during the course of a rape by Arthur Beard, take place?

113 What sexual perversion characterized the 1983 murders of young men, in a Peak District beauty spot, by a gang of four men including Peter Murray?

114 How did twenty-year-old Gary Taken kill nineteen-year-old Tessa Howden during the course of a serious sexual assault at her home in 1986?

115 In which county did the 1986 slaying of Mrs Jeanne Sutcliffe and her eight-month-old baby, Heidi, by family friend Mrs Heather Arnold, take place?

116 How, precisely, did thirteen-year-old Ivy Lydia Wood die during the course of a rape by her drunken killer Arthur Beard in 1919?

117 In which county did the unsolved 1939 murder of eleven-year-old Pamela Coventry, sexually assaulted then strangled, take place?

118 How did the nineteen-year-old killer Paul Bostock, who pleaded guilty at Leicester Crown Court in 1984 to the brutal sex murders of Caroline Osborne and Amanda Weedon, actually kill his victims?

119 In which county did the 1986 murder of sixteen-year-old Julie Harrison, following a sex attack by eighteen-year-old John Hardie, take place?

120 What was the occupation of the subsequently convicted murderer, John Hardie, the eighteen-year-old who sexually assaulted then killed sixteen-year-old Julie Harrison in 1986?

Question Rating (R5)

121 In which county did the 1978 murder of thirteen-year-old schoolboy Carl Bridgewater, by a gang of robbers he had disturbed, take place?

122 In what type of establishment in Bermondsey, London, did murderer Edward Dwyer, a brush salesman, smash in the head of his three-month-old baby in full view of his companions, in 1843?

123 What had been the occupation of John Edward Allen at the time he killed seventeen-month-old Kathleen Woodward, at Burford, Oxfordshire, in 1937?

124 Where did Tessa Miriam Conroy secrete the corpse of her epileptic son John, following his murder at her hands in London in 1953?

125 How old was Constance Kent when, in 1860, she murdered one of the children living in her family home, for which crime she was sentenced to death?

126 What was the profession of Elizabeth Brownrigg, hanged at Tyburn in 1767 for the murder of one of her young servant girls?

127 How did Alice East kill her own baby Alice Kathleen, at the village of Girton, Cambridgeshire, in 1908?

128 Whose child did thirty-six-year-old Louise Masset murder in London in 1899?

129 What was the occupation of twenty-two-year-old Peter Griffiths, convicted of the horrendous 1948 murder of three-year-old June Anne Devaney, near Blackburn, Lancashire?

130 Of how many murders was the multiple killer Michael Lupo convicted at his Old Bailey trial in 1987?

131 What is the name of the only victim of the infamous murderess Myra Hindley whose body has never been discovered?

132 How old was Francis Savill Kent when, in 1860, he was murdered in his family home by Constance Kent?

133 From which branch of the armed services was the subsequently convicted murderer Neville George Clevely Heath dismissed, in 1937, for disciplinary offences?

134 Of whom was Samuel Savill Kent, father of the notorious Victorian murderess Constance Kent, reputed to be the illegitimate son?

135 What distinctive method of killing his victims did John Francis Duffy employ throughout 1985 and 1986?

136 What was the occupation of Samuel Savill Kent, the father of murderess Constance Kent, who in 1860 killed one of the children living in their family home?

137 How many children did the murderer John Thomas Straffen, convicted in 1952, kill in total?

138 What distinctive type of vehicle, popular in the 1960s, was found near the battered body of sixty-year-old William Elliott, killed outside Chesterfield in 1960 by Michael Copeland?

139 At the 1873 trial of child poisoner Mary Ann Cotton, what sort of evidence was introduced by the prosecution to refute her claim that the whole incident was a terrible accident?

140 In which city did the multiple child killer John Thomas Straffen murder two little girls, within a month, in 1951?

141 How many young men did Peter Murray kill on successive days near Buxton, in the Peak District, in 1983, while in company with three others?

142 Which book, given to her by an aunt in 1958, was to play its part in convicting child killer Myra Hindley in 1966, when it was found to contain a left-luggage ticket?

143 What was the occupation of Richard Nilsson who was subsequently convicted of the 1968 murder of eight-year-old Christopher Sabey?

144 What was the nationality of the convicted child killer Louise Masset's lover, whom she was on her way to meet when she committed her crime in 1899?

145 From what, relatively rare, illness was it suggested that the convicted child killer Beverley Allitt, sentenced to life imprisonment in 1993, may have been suffering?

146 To which coastal resort was child murderer Louise Masset en route when she committed her crime in 1899?

147 Which infamous multiple sex killer wrote to his parents, shortly before he was executed, 'My only regret at leaving the world is that I have been damned unworthy of you both'?

148 With what, is it believed, did Michael Douglas Dowdall make the series of small circular marks found on the body of his victim, Veronica Murray, in 1958?

149 Which famous actor occupied the suite at the Westbury Hotel, Mayfair, broken into in 1958 by killer Michael Douglas Dowdall who left a number of clues to his identity?

150 By what unusual method did Adam Stein kill his child victim Collette Gallacher, in his home, leading to his imprisonment for life at Northampton Crown Court in 1986?

CHAPTER EIGHT

SCENES OF CRIME

Question Rating (R1)

1 Which infamous multiple murderer carried out his crimes at 10, Rillington Place, Notting Hill, London?

2 In which area of London, did the assailant known as 'Jack the Ripper' murder and mutilate five women, between August and November 1888?

3 Where, precisely, in London, was the Conservative MP Airey Neave assassinated in 1979?

4 What was the name of the public house in Whitechapel, East London, where, in 1966, Ronald Kray shot dead the small-time crook George Cornell?

5 In which city did the multiple murderers William Burke and William Hare operate between 1827 and 1828?

6 Outside what type of establishment was David Blakely shot dead by his lover, Ruth Ellis, in Hampstead, London, in 1955?

7 In which part of the London family home were the remains of Dr Crippen's victim discovered in 1910?

8 What was the name given, from the scene of the crimes, to the series of horrific murders which terrorized the East End of London in December 1811?

9 Where in London in 1812 did John Bellingham shoot dead the Prime Minister, the Right Honourable Spencer Perceval?

10 What was the name of the wife of the *News of the World* Deputy Chairman who was kidnapped in 1969 and subsequently murdered by the brothers Arthur and Nizamodeen Hosein?

11 In what type of location, in Croydon, was police constable Sidney Miles shot dead by Christopher Craig in November 1952?

12 What eventually happened, in 1911, to the tenement building in Sidney Street, East London, where a number of anarchists fought a gun battle with police and soldiers, bringing to an end the siege?

13 At what infamous London address were the bodies of Beryl and Geraldine Evans, whom Timothy John Evans initially confessed to having murdered, eventually discovered in 1949?

14 In which city did the inveterate criminal Patrick Carraher twice commit murder, the second leading to his execution in 1946?

15 Where, in Yarmouth, was the body of Mary Jane Bennett discovered in 1900, her husband Herbert John Bennett having strangled her?

16 What is the name of the stiffening process which affects the body of a murder victim, is usually completed within twelve hours and wears off after about thirty-six hours?

17 What was the name of the Brighton hotel where, in 1984, five people were murdered by a member of the Irish Republican Army while attempting to assassinate the entire British Cabinet?

18 Where, in London, was the body of the Italian financier, Roberto Calvi, at first thought to be a suicide victim but later the subject of an open verdict at a second inquest, discovered?

19 How, precisely, did Salem Ahmed Hassan murder the former Prime Minister, General Abdul Razzak Al-Naif outside London's International Hotel in 1978?

20 By what classic piece of forensic evidence was the IRA bomber Patrick Magee identified as the man responsible for the 1984 assassination attempt on the British Cabinet in Brighton, Sussex?

21 When WPC Yvonne Fletcher was shot dead in St James's Square, London in 1983, from which country's diplomatic premises were the bullets that killed her allegedly fired?

22 In a celebrated case, which famous politician's secretary did the hapless and quite mad Daniel MacNaughton shoot dead, between Downing Street and Whitehall, in London in 1843?

23 In what nostalgic London venue, which sadly no longer exists, did the young but mentally unbalanced Jack Tratsart attempt to shoot dead some family members at his own birthday party in 1945?

24 What was the popular name given to the crime kit, produced in the mid 1920s as a result of the contribution of the great pathologist Sir Bernard Spilsbury and taken by police officers to the scenes of murder inquiries?

25 In what type of terrain in Cheshire, in 1983, was the skull of a woman discovered which, although it was not the victim's, led to a confession by Peter Reyn-Bardt that he had killed his wife Malika several years before?

26 Where was the body of Stanislaw Skyut, murdered by his former business partner Michael Onufrejczyc at Cefn Hendre farm, Cwmdu, Wales, in 1953, eventually found?

27 What is the popular name given to the deposits of debris left, on a body or its clothing, when a firearm is discharged at close range to a victim?

28 In which county did the 1991 killings of several children by Beverley Allitt, take place?

29 Where exactly was Giorgi Markov murdered, by a poisoned bullet implanted from an umbrella tip, in London in 1978?

30 In which county did the 1985 farmhouse slayings of five close members of his family by Jeremy Bamber take place?

Question Rating (R2)

31 What was the connection between the scene of crime and the venue of the subsequent 1911 trial for murder of Edith Bingham, accused of killing her father, sister and brother, in that same year?

> **32** In the grounds of what type of building was three-year-old June Anne Devaney murdered by Peter Griffiths at Blackburn, Lancashire, in 1948?

33 When Archibald Brown was murdered by his son Eric at Rayleigh, Essex, in 1943, while sitting in his wheelchair, examination of the scene of the crime showed that he had been killed by what?

> **34** Where, specifically, did Evelyn Foster sustain her fatal injuries by fire at Otterburn, Northumberland, in 1931, resulting in a murder case which was never solved?

35 In what type of location was the body of Lesley Whittle, murdered by her kidnapper Donald Neilson, found hanging from a wire rope in 1975?

> **36** Which two brothers, subsequently convicted of murder, allegedly killed and disposed of their victim at Rooks Farm, Stocking Pelham, Hertfordshire, in 1970?

37 Where was the body of John Nisbet, robbed and shot by John Alexander Dickman in Northumberland in 1910, discovered almost immediately?

> **38** Which multiple murderer was living at 23 Cranley Gardens, Muswell Hill, London, the scene of some of his crimes, when he was arrested in 1983?

39 Where, in Britain, did the 1968 murder of Maxwell Robert Garvie, by his wife's lover Brian Tevendale, take place?

40 Forensic science, so often vital at the scene of a murder, is based on what very simple principle?

41 Where were the bodies of the poisoner Arthur Devereux's victims discovered in 1905?

42 In the 1921 killing of Irene Wilkins by Thomas Henry Allaway, what classic, yet crucial, clue was found on the ground, near the scene of the crime?

43 In what two different types of business premises did the infamous 'Ratcliffe Highway Murders', perpetrated in London by John Williams in 1811, take place?

44 Oscar Slater, later convicted of the 1908 murder of Miss Marion Gilchrist in Scotland, hurriedly left for New York after the killing. On which ship, later to be the subject of a terrible tragedy, did he sail?

45 The exhumation of a dead body is one of the methods by which police officers and scientists can detect foul play. Whose authority is needed for an exhumation, in Britain, whatever the purpose?

46 In which present-day county did the robber, murderer and mutinous First World War soldier Percy Toplis die in a hail of police bullets, while resisting arrest in June 1920?

47 What is the name of the discoloration process which affects the body of a murder victim soon after death and is a vital indication to detectives and pathologists that a body may have been moved, after death, from the true murder scene?

48 In what type of location in Scotland did the 1944 murder of Wolfgang Rosterg, by five of his associates, take place?

49 How did Jeremy Bamber slaughter five close members of his family at their farmhouse home in 1985?

50 Fanatics from which country planted a bomb in the left luggage office at King's Cross Station, London, which exploded killing Donald Campbell, a young Scottish doctor, in 1939?

51 Which human body tissue tends to outlast all others after death, thus often providing important clues in cases of murder?

52 With what murder weapon was Lieutenant Hubert George Chevis killed, by an unknown culprit, in Hampshire in June 1931?

53 In which area of London did the notorious Victorian poisoner Dr Thomas Neill Cream carry on his 'reign of terror'?

54 Outside the rear entrance to what type of London establishment did the 1897 murder, by stabbing, of William Terriss by Richard Prince take place?

55 At which famous London hotel did Madame Marie-Marguerite Fahmy shoot dead her husband Prince Ali Kamel Fahmy Bey, in the sensational murder case of 1923?

56 Where exactly was the dismembered body of Elsie Cameron found, following her murder by her fiancé Norman Thorne in 1924?

57 In which London suburb did the famous unsolved series of murders, by arsenic poisoning, of Edmund Creighton Duff and members of his family take place in 1928 and 1929?

58 Where were the bodies of teenagers Barbara Songhurst and Christine Reed discovered near Richmond, Surrey, after their murders by Alfred Charles Whiteway in 1953?

59 When the body of Bella Wright was found lying in a Leicestershire road in 1919, what clue near the body suggested that she had been the victim of a murderer rather than the casualty of a road accident?

60 In which cosmopolitan district of London was Max Kassel shot dead in a flat by Roger Marcel Vernon in January 1936?

Question Rating (R3)

61 In which seaside town did Sidney Harry Fox strangle his victim in 1929?

62 When, in 1949, John George Haigh murdered Mrs Olive Durand-Deacon, then attempted to dispose of her body, at his 'factory' in Crawley, Sussex, what decisive clue remained, allowing the police to identify the victim?

63 When, in 1953, George Albert Hall murdered then concealed the body of six-year-old Mary Hackett, in the crypt of a church in Halifax, Yorkshire, what items, left there to hide the smell of decomposition, eventually aroused the suspicion of investigating officers?

64 In which city did the multiple murderer Gordon Frederick Cummins operate during the Second World War blackout?

65 What conveyance, discovered in a garden shed, had been used to move the body of Lilian Chubb secretly from her home to a nearby hedge, following her death in 1958?

66 In what type of location, near Staines, Middlesex, was the body of George Heath, shot dead and robbed by Karl Gustav Hulten, discovered in October 1944?

67 Where did the 1947 murder by James Camb of the actress Gay Gibson, whose body was never found, take place?

68 Where had Ronald Evans left his victim Kathleen Heathcote, still alive after he raped her in Nottinghamshire in 1963, only to find on his return the following day that she was dead?

69 In what type of location were the bodies of the young girls Doreen Hearne and Kathleen Trendle, murdered by Harold Hill in Buckinghamshire in 1941, eventually discovered?

70 What type of weapons were used at the last authenticated fatal duel in England in 1852?

71 In what type of institution, in Hampshire, was Hubert George Chevis a resident when, in 1931, he was murdered by a still-unknown killer?

72 In what type of sporting location was Miss Edith Constance Drew-Bear shot and strangled by Percy Charles Anderson in 1934?

73 In which North of England city did the 1867 murder of Police Sergeant Charles Brett, by William O'Meara Allen and others, take place?

74 What weapons were used by Walter Sharpe and Gordon Lannon to murder Abraham Levine in his jeweller's shop in Leeds in 1949?

75 How did convicted murderer James Bairgrie controversially meet his death during a police siege in Philbeach Gardens, Earls Court, London, in 1985?

76 What is the highly appropriate name given to the Home Office computer system, available to police forces throughout the country, which can be used for large or major inquiries such as murders?

77 How did Elizabeth Brownrigg kill her domestic servant Mary Clifford in 1766, and so become one of that century's most hated murderesses?

78 What was the occupation of James Pope-Hennessey, murdered by three young men in his house in Ladbroke Grove, London, in 1974?

79 In what sort of receptacle was a time bomb left in the city of Coventry, by two members of the Irish Republican Army, Peter Barnes and James Richards, which exploded and killed five people in August 1939?

80 In what type of container was the body of eight-year-old Helen Priestly discovered in a tenement block in Aberdeen in 1934, following her murder by Mrs Jeannie Donald?

81 In what type of colourful location was the body of William Bissett, murdered by Joe Smith in Buckinghamshire in 1947, hidden for some time after the crime?

82 In which London street, near Wormwood Scrubs prison, were three police officers shot dead while questioning suspects in August 1966?

83 In the series of unsolved murders of prostitutes carried out in London between 1964 and 1965 by the so-called killer 'Jack the Stripper', traces of what substance had been found on all the victims, leading police to believe they had located the place where the bodies had been left for some time?

84 At which London railway station did the killer Patrick Mahon deposit a Gladstone bag, containing items connected with his murder of Emily Beilby Kaye in 1924?

85 In a basement flat, in which part of London, was Jack McVitie stabbed to death by Reginald Kray in 1967?

86 Where, on her farmhouse near Saffron Walden, was the body of Camille Holland eventually discovered some time after her murder by Samuel Dougal in 1899?

87 Where, in her home, was the body of ninety-four-year-old Mrs Freeman Lee discovered following her murder by housebreaker George Russell at Maidenhead, Berkshire, in 1948?

88 Where was the body of Irene Wilkins, battered to death by Thomas Henry Allaway near the South Coast in 1921, eventually found?

89 On which infamous spot, where the bodies of two other little girls had also been found, did the murderer Raymond Leslie Morris leave the corpse of his victim, seven-year-old Christine Darby, in Staffordshire in 1967?

90 Where, in Edgware, Middlesex, were Leopold and Esther Goodman battered to death by their son-in-law Daniel Raven in 1949?

Question Rating (R4)

91 In which country in 1953 did Sergeant Frederick Emmett-Dunne murder his fellow Sergeant Reginald Watters in an army barracks?

92 In what type of building was Christina Bradfield battered to death by George Ball in Liverpool in 1913?

93 In the unsolved 1945 murder of Charles Walton at the foot of Meon Hill, near Lower Quinton, Warwickshire, with what had the victim's body been pinned to the ground in a field?

94 Where precisely was the convicted murderer James Bairgrie holding out during the 1985 police siege which ended with his death in Philbeach Gardens, Earls Court, London?

95 By what physical features might the scientific discipline of forensic odontology be able to identify a murderer from clues left at the scene?

96 When Reginald Ivor Hinks murdered his eighty-five-year-old father-in-law, James Pullen, near Bath, Somerset, in 1933, how did he try to disguise the crime as a classic case of suicide?

97 In what type of building was the Countess Krystyna Skarbeck stabbed to death by Dennis Muldowney in 1952?

98 In which famous London hotel did Tony Marriott stab to death his victim, Catherine Russell, in 1980?

99 Where was the body of murdered farmer Arthur Johnson found battered and floating in Huntingdonshire some ten days after his murder, in 1956, by Morris Arthur Clarke?

100 How was the body of the actress Gay Gibson, murdered in 1947 by James Camb, disposed of?

101 Where, specifically, in a London street, was the body of Armenian criminal Ruben Martirosoff discovered in 1945, following his murder by Marian Grondkowski and Henryk Malinowski?

102 In what sort of shop, in Surbiton, Surrey, was Ernest Percival Key stabbed to death by William Thomas Butler during the course of a robbery in 1938?

103 What nationality were both the victim and the assailant who took part in the last authenticated fatal duel in England in 1852?

104 The body of James Frederick Ellis, murdered in 1923 by Albert Edward Dearnley, was found under some bushes. How was his position consistent with his having died of suffocation?

105 Where, in London, was the home of fourteen-year-old Keighley Barton, abducted and subsequently murdered by Ronald William Barton in 1985?

106 In what type of premises was the body of thirteen-year-old Ivy Lydia Wood discovered, following her killing by Arthur Beard in 1919?

107 In which famous forest did the murder of Thomas Morris, a manservant, by the infamous highwayman Richard Turpin, take place in 1735?

108 In what type of conveyance did the celebrated 1867 North of England murder of Police Sergeant Charles Brett, by William O'Meara Allen and others, take place?

109 In which English coastal city did Edward Thomas Lee strangle his girlfriend Vera Bicknell in 1942?

110 In which city did James Pollard kill his victim Zoë Wade in 1984?

111 In what type of location was the body of nine-year-old Jacqueline Williams found, half strangled then drowned by subsequently convicted murderer David Burgess in 1967?

112 In 1940 what important forensic clue, lying near the body of his fifteen-year-old female victim Mary Hagan, had been left by the murderer Samuel Morgan?

113 In which city did the strangler Joseph Clark murder his former landlady, Alice Fontaine, in 1928?

114 Near which south coast resort was Edith Constance Drew-Bear shot, then strangled, by Percy Charles Anderson in 1934?

115 Near what natural geographic feature was the body of Chung Yi Miao's victim discovered in 1928?

116 In what type of location was the body of Linda Peacock, the victim of Gordon Hay, discovered in 1967?

117 Where did the 1857 murder of Andrew Rose by Captain Henry Rogers take place, resulting in Rogers' trial and execution at Liverpool in the same year?

118 From what sort of building had John Hall absconded shortly before he shot Philip Pawsey and George Hutchins to death in London in 1961?

119 In what type of location was the body of murdered schoolgirl Mona Tinsley eventually discoverd in 1937?

120 Approximately how long had the mummified corpse of Mrs Frances Knight been inside a landing cupboard, at a house in Rhyl, prior to its discovery in 1960?

Question Rating (R5)

121 In what type of location was the body of three-year-old Thomas Wood discovered, following his murder by Albert Edward Burrows in Derbyshire in 1923?

122 Where, specifically, was William Tripp shot dead by John Rogers, near Chew Magna, Avon, in July 1960?

123 In which Northern city was the body of six-year-old Barbara Waterhouse, murdered by Walter Lewis Turner, discovered in an alleyway in 1891?

124 What strong clues subsequently pointing to murderer David Greenwood were found at the scene of his crime in 1918, where he had strangled and killed Nellie Trew?

125 When Arthur Boyce shot dead his fiancée Elizabeth McLindon, a housekeeper, in Belgravia, London, in 1946, which VIP was shortly to become resident at the address?

126 A receipt for what, found at the home of Mrs Annie Louise Kempson, battered to death by Henry Daniel Seymour in 1931, helped lead to his apprehension?

127 On what sort of expedition was Lieutenant Cecil Hambrough engaged when he was shot dead in 1893, in a case where no one was ever convicted?

128 In an unsolved murder case of 1908, in what type of building, close to the victim's home, was Mrs Caroline Luard shot twice through the head at close range?

129 When the Pole Stanislaw Myszka battered to death Mrs Catherine McIntyre in Perthshire in 1947, why was the return half of a railway ticket, found near the scene of the crime, important in helping to identify the murderer?

130 Where were the bodies of Patrick Higgins' two small sons found, bound together with sash cords, nearly two years after he had murdered them in 1911, in West Lothian, Scotland?

131 What two items, proving to be vital clues, did the subsequently convicted murderer Michael George Hart drop at the scene of his crime, when, in 1976, he shot dead Angela Woolliscroft during the course of a robbery in Richmond, Surrey?

132 Where in London in 1948, was the cartoonist Harry Michaelson attacked by Harry Lewis, sustaining injuries which resulted in his death and Lewis' conviction for murder?

133 The body of Miss Christina Bradfield, brutally murdered by George Ball (alias Sumner) in 1913 and then hurriedly disposed of, was eventually identified by, among other things, a lucky charm round her neck. What three well-known symbols were on that charm?

134 Where in the family mansion in Wiltshire, in 1860, did Constance Kent leave the body of her young victim following his murder?

135 In what activity was twenty-seven-year-old William Theodore Brennan engaged when he shot dead farmer John Rowlands on Rowlands' own farm at Benyffordd, Mold, in 1925?

136 In an unsolved 1953 case, where was eighty-year-old spinster Emily Pye battered to death in Halifax, Yorkshire, during the course of a robbery?

137 What is unusual about the village of Ashopton, in the High Peak mountain range, where the naked body of Kathleen Heathcote was eventually discovered, following her murder in 1963 by Donald Evans?

> **138** When Frederick Rothwell Holt shot dead his mistress, Kitty Breaks in 1919, what two incriminating items, giving clues to his identity, were left at the scene of the crime?

139 In what type of location, left over from the Second World War, was the schoolboy Andrew Bonnick murdered by Malcolm Keith Williams, near Barry, Glamorganshire, in 1960?

> **140** In which area of Surrey did the last authenticated fatal duel in England take place in 1852?

141 When, in 1964, the extensively decomposed body of Peter Thomas was found in a wood, the evidence of the pathologist Professor Keith Simpson concerning the timing of his death proved crucial in the subsequent trial, for murder, of William Brittle. Which insect's life cycle formed the basis of the Professor's conclusion?

> **142** In what type of shop did the unsolved 1930 murder of Miss Margery Wren take place?

143 In the unsolved 1931 London murder of eleven-year-old Vera Page what clue of a medical nature was left at the scene of the crime?

> **144** On which island did the 1984 murder of Michael Robertson by Timothy John Funge-Smith take place?

145 In what type of premises was the body of Caroline Ellen Trayler discovered, following her killing by Dennis Edmund Leckey in 1943?

146 In what type of institution, in Surrey, had Mrs Margery Radford been poisoned, with arsenic, over a period of about three months culminating in her death in April 1949, a crime in which her husband Frederick Gordon Radford, who subsequently took his own life, was a suspect?

147 In what sort of building did George Kelly murder the manager Leonard Thomas and his assistant John Catterall during the course of a robbery in 1949?

148 Outside what type of building was Raymond Purdy shot dead in London, in 1959, by the subsequently convicted murderer Guenther Podola?

149 The murderess Catherine Hayes, who was convicted in 1725 of the slaying, in London, of her husband, which she had carried out with the help of two young lodgers, established which two records – a 'first' and a 'last'?

150 The manager of what type of establishment in the Mile End area of London, became the victim of one of his employees, John Stockwell, who in 1934 killed him, stole money from the safe and escaped to Great Yarmouth where he was finally arrested?

CHAPTER NINE

TRIALS, TRIBULATIONS AND ENDINGS

Question Rating (R1)

1 What is generally believed to have happened to the body of Mrs Muriel McKay, kidnapped and murdered by the Hosein brothers, Nizamodeen and Arthur, in 1969?

2 Why was the 1905 Old Bailey trial of the brothers Albert and Alfred Stratton, for the murder of Mr and Mrs Farrow in the same year, a landmark in terms of scientific evidence?

3 When Jeremy Bamber murdered five close members of his family, at their farmhouse home in 1985, one of his victims, his sister Mrs Sheila Caffel, was a former model once known by a name which came to be used for these killings. What was that name?

4 How was the Conservative MP Airey Neave assassinated in London in 1979?

5 In a trial for murder, what aspect of a defendant's behaviour is judged by application of the 'McNaghten Rules'?

6 At a 1929 inquest into the death of Alfred Oliver, a tobacconist found battered to death in his shop in Reading, Berkshire, Philip Yale Drew was subjected to a controversially searching examination by the coroner. What was Drew's nationality?

7 In which city did the 1937 trial of Roger Marcel Vernon, alias Georges Lacroix, for the murder a year earlier in London of Max Kassel, take place?

8 Mr Justice Wills, the judge at the trial of the accused poisoner Adelaide Bartlett in 1886 was, some ten years later, to preside over the celebrated and controversial trial of which great writer?

9 At her trial in 1926 for the murder of Lily Waterhouse, what extraordinary but untrue claim did the convicted killer Louie Calvert make before the judge passed sentence of death upon her?

10 The Coroners Act of 1887 was amended in 1926 to compel a coroner, in cases of murder, to sit with what?

11 Why did the 1954 trial of Michael Onufrejczyc for the murder of Stanislaw Skyut, at Glamorgan Assizes, make legal history?

12 In 1981, Bruce Lee pleaded guilty to twenty-six cases of manslaughter (later reduced on appeal to fifteen), making him then regarded as Britain's worst mass killer. How had he killed his victims?

13 The Homicide Act of 1957 removed the death penalty from all but how many categories of 'capital murder'?

14 What was the basis of multiple killer John George Haigh's defence plea at his 1949 murder trial, following the death of Mrs Olive Durand-Deacon?

15 How was the completion of a judicial execution customarily signalled to those members of the public waiting outside the prison?

16 In English criminal law what is the minimum age at which a defendant can be charged with murder?

17 At the 1928 trial of Beatrice Annie Pace, for the murder by arsenic poisoning of her husband Henry Pace at their Gloucestershire farm, by what accidental means did the defence successfully suggest that Pace had absorbed the poison, thus resulting in the return of a not guilty verdict?

18 What nationality were the infamous murderers and body snatchers, William Burke and William Hare, who plied their trade in the late 1820s?

19 What was the famous family name of three British executioners, Tom, Harry and Albert, who all came from Clayton, in Yorkshire?

20 What celebrated incident occurred in 1885 at Exeter Gaol, when John Lee, who was convicted of the 1884 murder of Emma Keyse at Babbacombe, near Torquay, was brought to the scaffold?

21 Which infamous multiple killer, executed in 1915, made use of a number of aliases, including Mr Love, Mr Rose and Mr Williams, while pursuing his murderous career?

22 What does the ancient verdict, returned at a coroner's inquest on an individual's death, of 'felo de se' signify?

23 Where did Ronald True, convicted of the 1922 murder of Gertrude Yates in London, finish his days, dying in 1951 at the age of sixty?

24 In which regiment of the British Army had Eddie Browning, convicted of the 1988 murder of a pregnant woman, Mrs Marie Wilks, on the M50 motorway near Tewkesbury, at one time served?

25 At his trial in 1959 for shooting dead Raymond Purdy in the same year, in London, what unusual, but eventually unsuccessful, defence did Guenther Fritz Erwin Podola advance in answer to the charge of murder?

26 In which country did the 1955 trial of Frederick Emmett-Dunne, for the murder in 1953 of Reginald Watters, take place?

27 At which famous Glasgow prison was the convicted murderer Patrick Carraher hanged in 1946?

28 In order to proceed against a defendant on a charge of murder in England, within what period of time must a victim die of the injuries inflicted by the accused person?

29 What is the name of the museum founded in 1875 and now housed at New Scotland Yard, London, which contains a fascinating collection of articles and exhibits connected with, among other things, famous British murders?

30 When attempting to trace the movements of murderers who have absconded abroad, use is often made of the 'International Criminal Police Organization'; by what name is this organization better known in Britain?

Question Rating (R2)

31 At the 1893 trial in Edinburgh of Alfred John Monson for the murder and attempted murder of Cecil Hambrough in the same year, what verdict was returned by the jury?

32 What, in common with many other convicted murderers, did Thomas Henry Allaway do on the night before his execution in August 1922?

33 At the 1931 trial of Alfred Arthur Rouse for murder, who, was it established, was the victim whose unrecognizable body was left by the killer near a small village, to be discovered by locals?

34 How did Stinie Morrison, convicted of the 1911 murder of Leon Beron in London, eventually die himself in 1921?

35 In what sort of institution was Frederick Nodder when eventually charged, in the same year, with the 1937 murder of eleven-year-old schoolgirl Mona Tinsley?

36 What famous miscarriage of justice occurred at the 1939 trial, in Dorchester, of Joseph Williams for the murder, earlier that year, of Walter Dinnivan?

37 Despite the final abolition of the death penalty for murder, in Britain, at the end of 1969, in which London prison is the scaffold still maintained?

38 For what reason was the conviction of Charles Ellsome, for the 1911 murder of Rose Render in London, subsequently set aside by the Court of Criminal Appeal?

39 What verdicts were returned in the sensational 1935 trial of George Percy Stoner and Alma Rattenbury for the murder, in the same year, of her husband Francis Rattenbury?

40 The old verdict of a coroner's jury, of 'murder by person or persons unknown', was abolished in 1977. By what modern form of words was it replaced?

41 What is 'Evidence of System', sometimes introduced by the prosecution in British murder trials?

42 What statute makes murder a criminal offence in England?

43 At the trial of Gunner Dennis Edmund Leckey, accused of the 1943 killing of Caroline Ellen Trayler, what basic right of the defendant, under English law, did the trial judge wrongly comment on, leading the Court of Appeal subsequently to hear the case?

44 Which organization, at an inquest, questioned the tactics of the police, following the 1985 death in London of convicted murderer James Bairgrie?

45 What was the occupation of Eddie Browning, convicted of the 1988 murder of a pregnant woman, Mrs Marie Wilks, on the M50 motorway near Tewkesbury?

46 How did John Williams, perpetrator of the horrific 'Ratcliffe Highway Murders', in London in 1811, meet his death in Coldbath Fields Prison before he could come to trial?

47 When Oscar Slater, later convicted of the murder of Miss Marion Gilchrist in Scotland in 1908, was arrested in New York, USA, why were extradition proceedings never instigated?

48 From what public office, paradoxically, had John Price fallen before he was executed in 1718 for beating to death elderly Elizabeth White, in the City of London, after she resisted his attempt to rape her?

49 What was historically significant about the 1868 execution of Michael Barrett for the killing of four innocent passers-by during an unsuccessful attempt at a prison escape, in London, in the same year?

50 What was the occupation of the bisexual Archibald Hall (alias Roy Fontaine) who killed his employer the retired Labour MP Walter Scott-Elliot, in the late 1970s?

51 The sentence of 'penal servitude for life' was abolished in Great Britain in 1948 and replaced by what?

52 By what means was it alleged, at her 1911 trial, that Edith Bingham had murdered her brother, sister and father over a period of nine months in that same year?

53 What peculiarly 'female' reason did both the accused Victorian poisoners, Florence Maybrick and Madeleine Smith, advance for their legitimate possession and use of arsenic?

54 What was out of the ordinary about the 1983 appeal against conviction of Bruce Lee, for some of the twenty-six manslaughters to which he had pleaded guilty in 1981?

55 Which BBC television series highlighted the case of the squatter Mervyn John Russell, convicted in 1977 of stabbing to death Jane Bigwood at a block of flats in London, and led to his case being taken up by the organization 'Justice' and his eventual release by the Court of Appeal in 1982?

56 What nationality were the six men, subsequently executed for the murder, by beating to death, of Wolfgang Rosterg in Scotland in 1944?

57 Which famous murderer, when sentenced to death at Manchester Assizes in 1920, is alleged to have said, 'Well, that's over. I hope my tea won't be late'?

58 What does the common-law defence of 'autrefois convict', raised and rejected at the 1949 trial of Leonard Jack Thomas for the murder of his wife Florence, actually mean?

59 How did the subsequently convicted murderer Patrick Magee spectacularly murder five people in Brighton in 1984?

60 At the Old Bailey Mrs Elvira Dolores Barney was charged with, but acquitted of the murder of her lover, Michael Scott Stephen, in London in 1932. Where did she eventually die four years later?

Question Rating (R3)

61 At the 1915 Old Bailey trial of George Joseph Smith, for the murder of Bessie Mundy, what spectacular courtroom demonstration resulted in a nurse having to be given artificial respiration?

> **62** Which parts of the multiple killer John Donald Merrett (alias Ronald John Chesney), who committed suicide in 1954, are now in Scotland Yard's Black Museum?

63 In which country did the 1892 execution of the multiple murderer and confidence trickster Frederick Bayley Deeming take place?

> **64** In the 1920 trial of Ronald Light, for the murder of the twenty-one-year-old factory worker Bella Wright in Leicestershire the year previously, what mode of transport, did it emerge, was being used by both the accused and the dead girl on the day of her death?

65 Why did the 1962 trial of James Hanratty at Bedford Assizes, for the murder of Michael Gregsten, take its place in English criminal legal history?

> **66** At the 1952 Old Bailey trial of Christopher Craig for the murder of Sidney Miles, in the same year, what sentence was passed on him after the jury's verdict of guilty was returned?

67 Before what type of court, in 1955, was Frederick Emmett-Dunne found guilty of the 1953 murder of Reginald Watters?

68 Following his conviction at the Old Bailey in 1948 for the murder of Nathaniel Edgar earlier that year in London, why was the sentence of death passed on Donald George Thomas not carried out?

69 In which city was the notorious highwayman and murderer Richard Turpin executed in 1739?

70 Following his conviction at the Old Bailey in 1939 for the murder, earlier that year in London of Georgina Hoffman, where did Arthur James Mahoney eventually die?

71 What was the profession of Gerald Richards who, in 1980, shot Gail Kinchin in Birmingham, her subsequent death leading to the eventual conviction of David Pagett for her manslaughter?

72 What was historic in the Court of Criminal Appeal's decision to set aside the conviction of Charles Ellsome, for the 1911 murder of Rose Render in London, and release him?

73 Under British justice if, in a murder trial, an accused person raises a defence of 'accidental death', what type of evidence is the prosecution at liberty to place before the court?

74 In which prison, in Kent, is the infamous child killer Myra Hindley, convicted in 1966, now incarcerated?

75 What was the very novel and peculiar way in which the murderer Arthur Charles Mortimer killed his victim, Mrs Phyllis Oakes, on a railway bridge in Hampshire in 1935?

76 From which Communist country was Giorgi Markov a defector, when he was murdered in London in 1978?

77 What devastating evidence of premeditation was contained in a letter, seeking employment, written by the multiple poisoner Arthur Devereux, prior to his victim's death in 1905?

78 Of which notorious organization, in Ireland, had, the 1933 killer of Walter Spatchett, Samuel James Furnace, been a member just after the Great War?

79 When Colin Kemp was acquitted of the murder by strangulation of his wife Ellen, at his Old Bailey trial in 1986, his was seen as a case of 'automatism', whereby he had killed in his sleep. What had he been dreaming that he was doing?

80 The poisoner George Chapman was executed in 1903. What was his real name?

81 What record was achieved by the 1959 trial at Winchester Assizes of Brian Cawley, for the murder of Rupert Steed?

82 What change in the law of evidence, in relation to that of accomplices, was brought about following the 1953 trial and conviction for murder of John Michael Davies for the 'Clapham Common Murder'?

83 Following his 1943 Old Bailey trial for the murder of Mrs Ellen Symes, in the previous year, to where was the killer, Reginald Buckfield, originally sentenced to death, eventually committed?

84 Why was it decided, at committal proceedings, that it was not possible to try Frederick Emmett-Dunne before an English court for the 1953 murder of Reginald Watters?

85 When the Criminal Justice Act came into effect in 1964, what important new power did it give to the Court of Criminal Appeal, a power which might have proved useful some thirteen years earlier in the case of Alf Burns and Ted Devlin, convicted of murder at Liverpool Assizes?

86 At a 1979 trial at St Albans Crown Court, what sexual perversion did it emerge that Frederick Chapman, killed by his wife Margaret and her lover Peter West, was wont to indulge in?

87 From which university did the infamous child killer Myra Hindley, convicted in 1966, gain a BA Degree in Humanities?

88 What former high-ranking position had been held by Field Marshal Sir Henry Wilson, who was gunned down in a London street by two ex-soldiers in 1922?

89 For whom was the political defector Giorgi Markov working when he was murdered in London in 1978?

90 What forensic milestone was achieved at the 1911 Old Bailey murder trial of George Baron Pateman?

Question Rating (R4)

91 Which famous murderer, convicted in the 1940s at Winchester Assizes, had his death sentence commuted to life imprisonment after the House of Commons voted to suspend the death sentence?

92 At a 1929 inquest into the death of Alfred Oliver, a tobacconist found battered to death in his shop in Reading, Berkshire, Philip Yale Drew was the subject of a controversially searching examination by the coroner. What was Drew's occupation?

93 In which country did the multiple murderer John Donald Merrett, alias Ronald John Chesney, commit suicide in 1954?

94 At his trial in 1943 for the murder, in the same year, of his invalid father Archibald Brown, what verdict did the jury return in the case of Eric Brown?

95 At his trial for the murder of Mrs Catherine McIntyre, which resulted in his execution in Perth, Scotland, in 1948, what vital piece of forensic evidence helped to secure a conviction against Stanislaw Myszka?

96 At the 1986 trial, at Leeds Crown Court, of Ian and Allyson Kirk for the murder of seventy-five-year-old Ivy Preston at her home, in the previous year, what, did it emerge, was the apparent motive for their crime?

97 On leaving where, in 1929, was William Henry Podmore arrested and charged with the murder, earlier in the same year, of Vivian Messiter?

98 Following his conviction in Oxford, in 1922, for the murder of Sarah Blake earlier that year in Oxfordshire, why was the death sentence not passed on Jack Hewett?

99 By what colourful name were the trio of pathologists Keith Simpson, Donald Teare and Francis Camps often referred to by the police and privately by the Press?

100 Why precisely did John Hall, who had shot dead Philip Pawsey and George Hutchins in London in 1961, never come to trial on those charges?

101 At a 1929 inquest into the death of Alfred Oliver, a tobacconist found battered to death in his shop in Reading, Berkshire, Philip Yale Drew was the subject of a controversially searching examination by the coroner. What was the eventual verdict of the jury?

102 When the death sentence, passed on convicted murderer Albert Edward Dearnley for the 1923 killing of James Frederick Ellis, was commuted to penal servitude for life his coffin was used for another murderer, Abraham Goldenberg, hanged in 1924. What profession did Dearnley and Goldenberg also share?

103 When Ernest Brown was executed in 1934 for the murder of Frederick Morton in Yorkshire a year earlier, as he fell through the trap he was heard to mutter 'ought to burn' or 'Otterburn'. Why is this thought to be significant?

104 Approximately what percentage of criminals sent to Broadmoor Hospital for offences which are a danger to the public, and who are then released, subsequently commit similar crimes?

105 When, in 1950, George Kelly was tried at Liverpool Assizes for the murder by shooting, the previous year, of Leonard Thomas and John Bernard Catterall, how did his defence counsel Rose Heilbron make English legal history?

106 What did the Criminal Lunatics Act of 1844 ensure, as far as capital punishment was concerned?

107 At their trial in 1853, at Kingston Assizes, Surrey, four Frenchmen were convicted of the manslaughter of one of their fellow countrymen the year before, following what type of ancient but illegal activity?

108 In the 1911 trial of Stinie Morrison for the murder of Leon Beron in London, the counsel for his defence, by means of questions unconnected with the issue before the court, showed prosecution witnesses to be of doubtful character. What did this allow the prosecuting counsel under the Criminal Evidence Act of 1898, to do?

109 For what motive, peculiar to that period of Britain's history, was a young boy from Lincolnshire drowned by John Bishop and Thomas Head, alias Williams, in London's East End in 1831?

110 During the 1911 Old Bailey trial of Stinie Morrison for the murder of Leon Beron, in the same year, in London, what happened to the victim's brother, Solomon, during the final speech for the defence?

111 What was the profession of Percy Mapleton, who was executed in 1881 for the murder, by stabbing and shooting, of Frederick Gold on a journey between London and Brighton?

112 What was the occupation of Emmanuel Marshall, brutally murdered with his entire family in Denham Village, Middlesex, by a former casual employee, John Owen, in 1870?

113 When the remains of Marie Stuart were discovered by chance in 1961, a coroner's jury found that she had been murdered and that evidence pointed to Everard George Shotton as a possible suspect. When Shotton's whereabouts were discovered, why was he never charged with the offence?

114 How did the Anatomy Act of 1830 (Warburton's Act) effectively put a stop to the private trade of 'body-snatchers' such as Burke and Hare?

115 Following the 1951 trial and conviction, at Liverpool Assizes, of Alf Burns and Ted Devlin for the murder, a year previously, of Beatrice Alice Rimmer, how was legal history made in relation to an appeal by their counsel to introduce new evidence at this stage?

116 At a 1979 trial at St Albans Crown Court how did it emerge was the battered body of Frederick Chapman disposed of by his wife Margaret and her lover Peter West in 1979, allegedly to make his death appear to be either suicide or an accident?

117 When he was tried for the 1765 killing of a Mr Chaworth in a sword fight, Lord Byron, the uncle of the great poet, on being found guilty of manslaughter entered a plea of 'Benefit of Clergy'. What did this medieval ritual mean?

118 What was worthy of note about the 1950 committal proceedings for murder, in which a local labourer, who had found the strangled corpse of Mrs John Woodhouse in Arundel Park in 1948, was discharged due to insufficient evidence?

119 Of which country was General Abdul Razzak Al-Naif, assassinated in London in 1978, the former Prime Minister?

120 What did the spectacular courtroom command of her counsel Sir Patrick Hastings to, 'Pick up that revolver, Mrs Barney' and her subsequent action, demonstrate to the jury and help acquit her of the charge of murdering her lover, Michael Scott Stephen, at her 1932 Old Bailey trial?

Question Rating (R5)

121 At his 1937 trial, for the murder of Max Kassel in London the previous year, Roger Marcel Vernon, alias Georges Lacroix was, in addition to ten years' imprisonment, sentenced to twenty years' banishment; to where?

122 In order to commit murder in English Law there must not only be what is called an 'actus reus' (a guilty act) but it must also be accompanied by evidence of 'mens rea'. What is 'mens rea'?

123 What was notable about the execution of the murderers Fowler, Milsom and Seaman on 9 June 1896, at Newgate Prison, London?

124 Why were the 1946 divorce proceedings concerning Walter Graham Rowland, eventually executed at Strangeways Prison for murdering Olive Balchin, held 'in camera'?

125 During his trial at the Old Bailey in 1922, for the murder of Gertrude Yates in London in the same year what did the warders sitting behind Ronald True see him spend his time doing?

126 The multiple murderer and confidence trickster Frederick Bayley Deeming was tried in a foreign country, in 1892, for the murder of Emily Mather. What high office did his defence counsel, Alfred Deakin, go on to attain?

127 What was the name of the man who, following the 1962 execution of James Hanratty for the murder of Michael Gregsten, made the claim that he was involved in the killing and not Hanratty?

128 How did Richard Hemming, a Cheshire carpenter and hired assassin who, in 1806, murdered the Reverend George Parker in Worcestershire, meet his own untimely and apt end that same year?

129 Following the execution of the notorious poisoner Dr Thomas Neill Cream at Newgate Prison in 1892, to whom were his clothes and belongings sold for £200?

130 When Christopher Craig, convicted of the 1952 murder of Sidney Miles, was eventually released on licence in 1963, in which county did he settle?

131 How many people were convicted at Bodmin Assizes in 1931 of the murder, by poisoning, a year earlier of Mrs Alice Thomas, at a farm in Cornwall?

132 When the retired business woman Kathleen Calhaen was convicted, in 1984, following the killing of Mrs Shirley Rendell, what method had she employed to carry out her crime?

133 By what abhorrent means did Haydn Evan Evans, kill seventy-six-year-old Mrs Rachel Allan, near her home in the Rhondda Valley, South Wales, in 1947?

134 How long, approximately, was the 1952 Old Bailey trial of Dennis Muldowney for the murder of Countess Krystyna Skarbeck in London earlier that year?

135 When Henry Fowler and Albert Milsom, convicted of the 1896 murder of Henry Smith in London, were hanged at Newgate Prison in the same year, what unusual event befell the hangman's assistant?

136 When Susan Newell was hanged at Duke Street Prison, Glasgow, in 1923 for the murder of thirteen-year-old John Johnston earlier in the same year, what usual part of the proceedings did she refuse to countenance?

137 In a celebrated 1863 murder case in Derbyshire, how did George Townley kill his fiancée 'Bessie' Goodwin, who had jilted him?

138 What dubious distinction, in relation to his execution at Armley Gaol, Leeds, is held by Walter Lewis Turner who, in 1891, murdered six-year-old Barbara Waterhouse?

139 How did Walter Lewis Turner who, in 1891, had killed six-year-old Barbara Waterhouse and dumped her body in an alleyway, initially become a police suspect?

140 When, in 1933, the massive manhunt for Samuel James Furnace, wanted for the killing that year in London of Walter Spatchett, was in full flow, what extreme order was given – this being a 'first' for the Metropolitan Police and requiring the approval of Commissioner Lord Trenchard?

141 What was the name of the little girl murdered and literally torn to pieces by a clerk called Frederick Baker, in Alton, Hampshire, in 1867, whose name has entered the English language as a slang phrase?

142 When, in 1981, Paul Corrigan, a man with previous convictions for violent sex offences against boys, waylaid, tortured and then killed thirteen-year-old schoolboy John Haddon in a flat near Birmingham, what was he 'on'?

143 What macabre article, belonging to Paul Corrigan, was discovered by the authorities in Maidstone Gaol before he was released and subsequently killed a thirteen-year-old schoolboy, in a flat near Birmingham, in 1981?

144 What was noteworthy about the execution of six foreigners, hanged at Pentonville Gaol, London, in 1945 for the murder, a year previously in Scotland, of Wolfgang Rosterg?

145 How had Mrs Shirley Rendell actually been killed, at her home, by Julian Zajac, which act led to his conviction, along with his female associate, at Winchester Crown Court in 1984?

146 What was shown to a jury, for the first time in a British murder case, at Kingston Assizes, during the trial of August Sangret for the killing of his girlfriend Joan Wolfe in 1943?

147 When Lord Ferrers was executed at Tyburn in 1760 for the murder of his steward John Johnson, in the same year, of what did he become the 'last'?

148 In 1960, in a case which was eventually to go to the House of Lords for a decision on the legal interpretation of the objective test of intent, how did 'gypsy' Jim Smith murder Police Constable Leslie Meehan who was in the execution of his duty?

149 What was noteworthy about Michael John Davies' stay in the condemned cell following his conviction for the murder of John Beckley on Clapham Common in 1953?

150 When Arthur Hall, a local farmworker, was convicted at Nottingham Crown Court of the senseless murders of two teenagers, Peter Thompson and Lorraine Underwood, in 1979, how did he, filled with remorse, apparently attempt to injure himself in the dock while sentence was being passed?

PART TWO

CLUES

CHAPTER ONE

CLUES

Question Rating (R1)

1   (i)   It was the first arrest
          at sea for murder
    (ii) It was the first arrest
          for murder prior to
          the discovery of a
          body
    (iii) It was the first time
          a wireless telegraph
          had been used to
          effect the arrest of a
          murder suspect

2   (i)   Not guilty
    (ii) Guilty
    (iii) Guilty of
          manslaughter

3   (i)   Her sister Loretta
    (ii) Her brother-in-law
          Michael
    (iii) Her husband James

4   (i)   Cyanide
    (ii) Arsenic
    (iii) Strychnine

5   (i)   His wife
    (ii) His mother
    (iii) His son

6   (i)   Belle Elmore
    (ii) Margaret Godlewski
    (iii) Ethel le Neve

7   (i)   He was a policeman
    (ii) He was a solicitor
    (iii) He was a teacher

8   (i)   Karl Lewis
    (ii) Graham Young
    (iii) Peter Sutcliffe

9   (i)   As a nun
    (ii) As a badly burnt
          invalid
    (iii) As a young boy

10 (i)   Her husband
    (ii) Her daughter
    (iii) Her lover

11 (i)   Ethel Barrymore
    (ii) Belle Elmore
    (iii) Melanie Starr

12 (i) In a bowl of cream
(ii) In a chocolate sweet injected with poison
(iii) In a bedtime drink

13 (i) He was Canadian
(ii) He was American
(iii) He was French

14 (i) Devon
(ii) The Midlands
(iii) The North-East

15 (i) A pawnbroker's
(ii) A nursing home
(iii) A laundry

16 (i) Dr Thomas Neill Cream
(ii) Dr Hawley Harvey Crippen
(iii) Arthur Chapman

17 (i) 'Champagne Charlie'
(ii) 'Killarney Kate'
(iii) 'Rose of the Rhondda'

18 (i) The discovery of bones
(ii) An anonymous letter
(iii) A post-mortem examination

19 (i) USA
(ii) Poland
(iii) Australia

20 (i) Her children, Lily and Ernest
(ii) Her husband, Frederick Bryant
(iii) Her neighbour, Lucy Ostler

21 (i) He was Belgian
(ii) He was Canadian
(iii) He was French

22 (i) Classical singing
(ii) The ballet
(iii) Mime

23 (i) Canada
(ii) USA
(iii) Scotland

24 (i) Dr William Smith
(ii) Dr John Bodkin Adams
(iii) Dr Thomas Cream

25 (i) Sussex
(ii) Surrey
(iii) Shropshire

26 (i) His baby's nurse
(ii) His maid
(iii) His bookkeeper and secretary

27 (i) Mary Ann Cotton
(ii) Adelaide Bartlett
(iii) Barbara Kirkam

28 (i) An ecclesiastical
        court
     (ii) A coroner's court
     (iii) A court martial

29 (i) Street urchins
     (ii) Prostitutes
     (iii) Domestic servants

30 (i) Major
     (ii) Colonel
     (iii) Captain

Question Rating (R2)

31 (i) It is still not known
     (ii) In a condom
     (iii) Swallowed under
           the influence of
           hypnosis

32 (i) Less than 6 per cent
     (ii) Less than 10 per
           cent
     (iii) Less than 15 per
           cent

33 (i) 'The Whitechapel'
        murders
     (ii) 'The Ratcliffe
           Highway' murders
     (iii) The 'Brides in the
           Bath' murders

34 (i) Cyanide
     (ii) Mercury
     (iii) Arsenic

35 (i) Sergeant Major
     (ii) Lance Sergeant
     (iii) Master Sergeant

36 (i) Cumbria
     (ii) Cornwall
     (iii) Dorset

37 (i) In a brothel
     (ii) In a public house
     (iii) In a railway station

38 (i) Dissolving her
        cosmetics in water
     (ii) Soaking pieces of
           wallpaper in water
     (iii) Soaking fly-papers
           in water

39 (i) Luton
     (ii) Halifax
     (iii) Brighton

40 (i) Broadmoor Hospital
     (ii) Rampton Hospital
     (iii) Selby Borstal

41 (i) Unpaid gambling
        debts
     (ii) A homosexual
           lovers' quarrel
     (iii) His adulterous
           association with the
           victim's wife

42 (i) Lancashire
     (ii) Lincolnshire
     (iii) Lanarkshire

43 (i) Arsenic
    (ii) Chloroform
    (iii) Salmonella bacilli

44 (i) His wife and their sons
    (ii) His mother and father-in-law
    (iii) His brother and sister

45 (i) A severe limp
    (ii) A false arm
    (iii) Crossed eyes

46 (i) That he was accidentally poisoned by the constituents of some wallpaper in his home
    (ii) That he had committed suicide
    (iii) That she had accidentally administered a dose of poison from a bottle she thought was medicine

47 (i) He was a farmer
    (ii) He was a bookkeeper
    (iii) He was a publican

48 (i) Both were Irish
    (ii) Both were Freemasons
    (iii) Both were dyslexic

49 (i) A cat
    (ii) A dog
    (iii) A rabbit

50 (i) He was a prizefighter
    (ii) He was a soldier
    (iii) He was a convict

51 (i) That he was Jesus Christ
    (ii) That he was 'Jack the Ripper'
    (iii) That it was impossible to kill him

52 (i) Their baby son
    (ii) Their classmates at school
    (iii) Their employer

53 (i) None
    (ii) Two
    (iii) Three

54 (i) As an osteopath
    (ii) As manager of a patent-medicine company
    (iii) As a veterinary surgeon

55 (i) He was a stockbroker
    (ii) He was a doctor
    (iii) He was a clergyman

56 (i) Not proven
(ii) Guilty but insane
(iii) Not guilty

57 (i) Morphine
(ii) Strychnine
(iii) Chloroform

58 (i) China
(ii) Australia
(iii) USA

59 (i) Walter Spatchett
(ii) Himself
(iii) Mrs Eva Furnace

60 (i) Arsenic
(ii) Strychnine
(iii) Caustic soda

Question Rating (R3)

61 (i) He was an insurance agent
(ii) He was a newspaper reporter
(iii) He was a banker

62 (i) Morphine
(ii) Antimony
(iii) Strychnine

63 (i) Her niece
(ii) Her cousin
(iii) Her sister

64 (i) He was the mayor
(ii) He was a doctor
(iii) He was the Chief of Police

65 (i) Arsenic
(ii) Strychnine
(iii) Cyanide

66 (i) He was a pawnbroker
(ii) He was a cotton broker
(iii) He was a stockbroker

67 (i) Strychnine
(ii) Cyanide
(iii) Arsenic

68 (i) An associate, Reginald Parker
(ii) His wife Cora Brinkley
(iii) Mr and Mrs Beck, his landlord's associates

69 (i) Lead
(ii) Antimony
(iii) Phosphorus

70 (i) He was a male nurse
(ii) He was a policeman
(iii) He was a teacher

71 (i) Insanity
(ii) Crime of passion
(iii) Mistaken identity

72 (i) LSD
(ii) Barbiturate
(iii) Arsenic

73 (i) Belgium
(ii) Canada
(iii) Jersey

74 (i) SS *Montrose*
(ii) MV *Orion*
(iii) SS *Laurentic*

75 (i) Consett, County
Durham
(ii) Chippenham,
Wiltshire
(iii) Neasden, London

76 (i) A boxing match
(ii) A horse race
meeting
(iii) A polo match

77 (i) The USA
(ii) Van Diemen's Land
(iii) Jamaica

78 (i) Strychnine
(ii) Chloroform
(iii) Antimony

79 (i) His foot
(ii) His teeth
(iii) His lungs

80 (i) Phosphorus
(ii) Morphine
(iii) Antimony

81 (i) A cup of tea
(ii) A meat pie
(iii) A bottle of bromo
salts

82 (i) Two servant girls
(ii) His wife and
mother-in-law
(iii) His twin sons

83 (i) To gain continued
access to his
children
(ii) To cover up a
fraudulent will
(iii) To gain money from
an insurance policy

84 (i) It permitted the use
at trial of the
uncorroborated
evidence of a co-
defendant
(ii) It allowed a
defendant to be
tried in London if he
were unlikely to get
a fair hearing in his
own county
(iii) It restricted the
prosecution from
relying entirely on
the evidence of a
spouse to gain a
conviction

85 (i) He was a fairground clown
(ii) He was a music hall singer
(iii) He was a gypsy

86 (i) Seventeen years old
(ii) Fifteen years old
(iii) Fourteen years old

87 (i) Antimony
(ii) Arsenic
(iii) Strychnine

88 (i) Two
(ii) Three
(iii) Five

89 (i) He was a chemist
(ii) He was a Wesleyan minister
(iii) He was a doctor

90 (i) In Melbourne, Australia
(ii) In Connecticut, USA
(iii) In Cape Town, South Africa

Question Rating (R4)

91 (i) Belladonna
(ii) Thallium
(iii) Arsenic

92 (i) Aberystwyth
(ii) Llandudno
(iii) Hay-on-Wye

93 (i) Alfred Brierley
(ii) Alfred Dodds
(iii) Arthur Sullivan

94 (i) Nicotine
(ii) Antimony
(iii) Strychnine

95 (i) He was the first British poisoner known to have used a hypodermic syringe on his victims
(ii) He was the first British poisoner known to have used thallium on his victims
(iii) He was the first British poisoner known to have used hypnosis on his victims

96 (i) Great Britain
(ii) USA
(iii) Canada

97 (i) Dartmoor Prison
(ii) Parkhurst Prison, Isle of Wight
(iii) Fort Leavenworth Prison, Kansas, USA

98 (i) Because he was the murderer

(ii) Because he was appalled at his wrong diagnosis, having failed to spot that she had been poisoned by morphine

(iii) Because he could not bring himself to accuse a fellow doctor of the crime

99 (i) Prussic acid

(ii) Lead

(iii) Formic acid

100 (i) An anonymous letter to the authorities

(ii) A newspaper article Pritchard wrote

(iii) His attempted suicide by poisoning

101 (i) Cigarettes

(ii) Oatmeal stout

(iii) Steak sandwiches

102 (i) Caustic soda

(ii) Bleach

(iii) Paraquat

103 (i) He was a bus driver

(ii) He was a chauffeur

(iii) He was a gardener

104 (i) Theft

(ii) Forgery

(iii) Blackmail

105 (i) Both were authors of books

(ii) Both were homosexual

(iii) Both were Freemasons

106 (i) It was the first time the poison hyoscine was involved in a murder trial

(ii) It was the first time that a poison believed undetectable in the body had been used

(iii) It was the first time the poison cocaine had been involved in a murder trial

107 (i) Because the evidence was too old

(ii) Because some of the victims had been accomplices

(iii) Because he did not take the witness stand

108 (i) Opium
(ii) Morphine
(iii) Nicotine

109 (i) A chemical firm
(ii) A photographic and optical equipment laboratory
(iii) A forensic laboratory

110 (i) Tobacco leaves
(ii) Bromide
(iii) Nitric acid

111 (i) Indecent assault
(ii) Forging medical prescriptions
(iii) Bigamous marriages

112 (i) He was a naval sickberth attendant
(ii) He was an army medical orderly
(iii) He was an air force nurse

113 (i) He was a teacher
(ii) He was a doctor
(iii) He was a circus clown

114 (i) He had escaped to Paraguay and could not be extradited

(ii) He had taken his own life with the same poison
(iii) The crime took place on the high seas and jurisdiction was in doubt

115 (i) Strychnine
(ii) Phosphorus
(iii) Nitirc acid

116 (i) A book on fungi
(ii) A chemistry set
(iii) A book on famous poisoners

117 (i) Holloway
(ii) Hull
(iii) Strangeways

118 (i) To attend her children's funeral
(ii) To get married
(iii) To give birth to a child

119 (i) Mercury
(ii) Prussic acid
(iii) Morphine

120 (i) Heidi Pender
(ii) Alice Yapp
(iii) Anna Dyer

Question Rating (R5)

121 (i) Her lover, Richard Collins
(ii) Her husband, Michael Barber
(iii) Her three children

122 (i) His landlady, Mrs Blume
(ii) His employer, John Wilson
(iii) His mother, Alice

123 (i) 'J. Winker'
(ii) 'J. Wanker'
(iii) 'J. Wonker'

124 (i) He was a butcher
(ii) He was a decorator
(iii) He was a jobbing gardener

125 (i) The lighthouse at Margate
(ii) The plinth of Nelson's column
(iii) Admiralty Arch

126 (i) Because she was insane
(ii) Because she had syphilis
(iii) Because she had turned to religion

127 (i) Five to ten victims

(ii) Ten to twenty victims
(iii) Over twenty victims

128 (i) Antimony
(ii) Insulin
(iii) Barbiturates

129 (i) He was an insurance salesman
(ii) He was a newspaper seller
(iii) He was a pedlar

130 (i) Arsenic
(ii) Opium
(iii) Lead

131 (i) Five or six
(ii) Nine or ten
(iii) Thirteen or fourteen

132 (i) Discrepancies in scientific, analytical tests
(ii) Another individual confessed to the crime
(iii) Smethurst was dying of cancer

133 (i) A poisoned chocolate cream
(ii) A poisoned cake
(iii) Poisoned fruit

134 (i) Cumbria
(ii) Cheshire
(iii) Cornwall

135 (i) 'The Hertfordshire
Scourge'
(ii) 'The Hadlands
Curse'
(iii) 'The Bovingdon
Bug'

136 (i) France
(ii) Germany
(iii) Spain

137 (i) A strychnine
capsule
(ii) Half the steel part of
his spectacles
(iii) A gold crucifix

138 (i) He was an army
officer
(ii) He was a
shopkeeper
(iii) He was a doctor

139 (i) Cumbria
(ii) Cheshire
(iii) Cornwall

140 (i) He became the only
blind man ever to be
hanged for murder
(ii) He became the only
solicitor ever to be
hanged for murder
(iii) He became the only
Channel Islander
ever to be hanged
for murder

141 (i) It was held at night
because of rioting in
Glasgow
(ii) It was the last public
hanging in Scotland
(iii) It was postponed
twice due to the
sudden deaths of
two successive
executioners

142 (i) That letters and a
photograph of his
mistress be buried
with him
(ii) That he be allowed
to become a Roman
Catholic
(iii) That he be allowed
to speak privately
with his former
mistress

143 (i) His mother-in-law
(ii) His sister
(iii) His daughter

144 (i) Chloroform
(ii) Cocaine
(iii) Arsenic

145 (i) Her father
(ii) Her lover William
Cranstoun
(iii) Her husband

146 (i) Arsenic
(ii) Cyanide
(iii) Morphine

(ii) *A Struggle for Justice*
(iii) *Poison Pen Letters*

147 (i) It was the first time that this charge had been preferred as a result of evidence from a cremated corpse
(ii) It was the first time that this charge had been preferred as a result of 'hearsay evidence'
(iii) It was the first time that this charge had been preferred as a result of video camera evidence

148 (i) *My Fifteen Lost Years*

149 (i) It was the first recorded charge of murder using liquid chloroform
(ii) It was the first recorded charge of murder using hypnosis
(iii) It was the first recorded charge of murder using gelatine capsules

150 (i) Leeds Assizes
(ii) The Central Criminal Court
(iii) Lewes Assizes

CHAPTER TWO

CLUES

Question Rating (R1)

1
  (i) Shock
  (ii) Heart failure
  (iii) Asphyxiation

2
  (i) 39 Hilldrop Crescent
  (ii) 10 Rillington Place
  (iii) 23 Cranley Gardens

3
  (i) Bristol
  (ii) Cardiff
  (iii) Glasgow

4
  (i) Father and daughter
  (ii) Husband and wife
  (iii) Brother and sister

5
  (i) To a female vagrant
  (ii) To a woman who died over 1500 years ago
  (iii) To a chimpanzee

6
  (i) John Haigh
  (ii) Neville Heath
  (iii) John Christie

7
  (i) A prostitute
  (ii) His wife
  (iii) A policeman

8
  (i) Wales
  (ii) Scotland
  (iii) London

9
  (i) His daughter
  (ii) His mother
  (iii) His wife

10
  (i) A gold chain
  (ii) An ankle bracelet
  (iii) A tiara

11
  (i) Korean
  (ii) British
  (iii) Chinese

12
  (i) He was a sadist
  (ii) He was homosexual
  (iii) He was a necrophiliac

13
  (i) Coventry
  (ii) Leeds
  (iii) Birmingham

14
  (i) Detention at Her Majesty's pleasure
  (ii) Life imprisonment
  (iii) Deportation order

15
  (i) By fire
  (ii) By a forged suicide note
  (iii) By a 'faked' hanging

16
  (i) Edward Marshall Hall
  (ii) Christmas Humphreys
  (iii) F. E. Smith

17
  (i) Greece
  (ii) Turkey
  (iii) Cyprus

18
  (i) A hat
  (ii) An overcoat button
  (iii) A glove

19
  (i) Amelia Dyer
  (ii) Amelia Sach
  (iii) Annie Waters

20
  (i) Burma
  (ii) India
  (iii) Siam

21
  (i) His job as a door-to-door salesman of Bibles
  (ii) His habit of quoting from the Bible
  (iii) His job as a Presbyterian Minister

22
  (i) Canada
  (ii) South Africa
  (iii) Australia

23
  (i) Police questioning of suspects and, in particular, of children and the educationally subnormal
  (ii) Police evidence in relation to 'Agents Provocateurs'
  (iii) The grading of circumstantial evidence

24
  (i) Witchcraft
  (ii) A sexual assault
  (iii) Suicide

25
  (i) One
  (ii) Two
  (iii) Three

26
  (i) They were all old women with no relatives
  (ii) They were all educationally subnormal
  (iii) They were all infants or children

27 (i) American
   (ii) Australian
   (iii) Canadian

28 (i) Water
   (ii) Soot
   (iii) Blood

29 (i) A bootlace
   (ii) A stocking
   (iii) His hands

30 (i) Mother-in-law
   (ii) Sister-in-law
   (iii) Stepmother

Question Rating (R2)

31 (i) In a car boot
   (ii) In a wardrobe
   (iii) On a cart

32 (i) Rape
   (ii) Grievous bodily
        harm
   (iii) Assault with intent
        to rob

33 (i) Sir Bernard
        Spilsbury
   (ii) Francis Camps
   (iii) Professor Keith
        Simpson

34 (i) Dental work
   (ii) Fingerprints
   (iii) Operation scars

35 (i) An army barracks
   (ii) A nurses' home
   (iii) A YWCA hostel

36 (i) It was never
        discovered
   (ii) Peter Manuel
   (iii) Donald Neilson

37 (i) Bedfordshire
   (ii) Nottinghamshire
   (iii) Sussex

38 (i) A silk scarf
   (ii) A stocking
   (iii) A shoelace

39 (i) Poole, Dorset
   (ii) Hove, Sussex
   (iii) Broadstairs, Kent

40 (i) An actor
   (ii) An artist
   (iii) A dancer

41 (i) Guilty of
        manslaughter
   (ii) Not guilty
   (iii) The jury could not
        reach a verdict

42 (i) They were mother-
        in-law and daughter-
        in-law
   (ii) They were sisters
   (iii) They were cousins

43 (i) His daughter, Geraldine
(ii) His lover, Ethel
(iii) A neighbour, Mary Williams

44 (i) Fingerprints
(ii) Dental records
(iii) Laundry marks on clothing

45 (i) Immediate release from prison
(ii) A posthumous free pardon
(iii) Leave to appeal to the House of Lords

46 (i) The United States Supreme Court
(ii) The United Nations
(iii) The British Broadcasting Corporation

47 (i) Phrenology
(ii) Carbon dating of the skulls
(iii) Comparison of the skulls with known photographs

48 (i) Liverpool
(ii) Glasgow
(iii) London

49 (i) Yoga
(ii) Tai Chi
(iii) Hypnosis

50 (i) The Army
(ii) The Royal Navy
(iii) The Royal Air Force

51 (i) By setting fire to it
(ii) By soaking it with acid
(iii) By dismembering it

52 (i) His brother
(ii) His sister
(iii) His mother

53 (i) Surrey
(ii) Essex
(iii) Northamptonshire

54 (i) Fingerprints
(ii) Footprints
(iii) Cigarette ends

55 (i) Yorkshire
(ii) Lancashire
(iii) Bedfordshire

56 (i) She set fire to it
(ii) She dismembered it
(iii) She put it in a vat of acid

57 (i) His hands
(ii) A pyjama cord
(iii) A dog's lead

58 (i) The tympanic bone
(ii) The hyoid bone
(iii) The sinoid bone

59   (i) Mexico
   (ii) Italy
   (iii) Spain

60   (i) The statement of an
      accomplice
   (ii) Circumstantial
      evidence
   (iii) Forensic evidence

Question Rating (R3)

61   (i) A teddy bear
   (ii) A note scrawled in
      ballpoint pen
   (iii) A bunch of flowers

62   (i) The Royal Navy
   (ii) The Army
   (iii) The Air Force

63   (i) A police cell in
      Clapham, London
   (ii) A Salvation Army
      hostel in Liverpool
   (iii) The forecourt of
      Paddington Station,
      London

64   (i) Because of a dying
      declaration
   (ii) Because of Rouse's
      confession, later
      published in the
      Daily Sketch
   (iii) Because of rope
      marks on the neck

65   (i) A necklace
   (ii) A bootlace
   (iii) A cravat

66   (i) The fact that she
      was infertile
   (ii) The colour of her
      eyes
   (iii) The fact that she
      was an alcoholic

67   (i) He was a chauffeur
   (ii) He was a hotel
      barman
   (iii) He was a teacher

68   (i) Identification by
      DNA records
   (ii) Identification by
      voice print
   (iii) Identification by
      dental bite marks on
      the victim

69   (i) The Grand Hotel
   (ii) The Metropole Hotel
   (iii) The Regency Hotel

70   (i) She was his wife
   (ii) She was his sister
      and accomplice
   (iii) She was his fiancée

71   (i) Cypriot
   (ii) German
   (iii) British

72 (i) Insanity
(ii) Self-defence
(iii) Provocation

73 (i) Her suspender belt
(ii) A pair of braces
(iii) Her victim's scarf

74 (i) That he had killed under the influence of demonic spirits
(ii) That he had killed in his sleep, therefore no crime had been committed
(iii) That he had killed under the influence of hypnosis

75 (i) She was his sister
(ii) She was his daughter
(iii) She was his common-law wife

76 (i) A public house
(ii) A ballroom
(iii) A church

77 (i) They were both carried out by Dr Keith Simpson
(ii) They were both carried out by Dr Francis Camps
(iii) They were both inconclusive

78 (i) An asphyxia

(ii) A binding
(iii) A ligature

79 (i) Because he was a drug addict
(ii) Because he was a spy
(iii) Because he was a bigamist

80 (i) Six months
(ii) Three months
(iii) One day and a half

81 (i) Fear of blackmail
(ii) A suspicion of infidelity on the part of his common-law wife
(iii) Monetary gain

82 (i) Fingerprints
(ii) Saliva residue
(iii) Hair fibres

83 (i) Austin
(ii) Vauxhall
(iii) Ford

84 (i) Because he held her underwater
(ii) Because he had drunk her blood
(iii) Because he had undressed first

85 (i) Surrey
(ii) Bedfordshire
(iii) Hampshire

86 (i) A request for him to stand on an identity parade
(ii) A request for a handwriting sample
(iii) A request for his fingerprints

87 (i) The victim's body had not been found and there was insufficient evidence for a charge of murder
(ii) The defendant was already under sentence of death for a previous murder
(iii) The defendant turned 'King's Evidence' to save himself

88 (i) Guilty of manslaughter
(ii) Guilty but insane
(iii) Guilty of causing grievous bodily harm

89 (i) Strips from a torn bed sheet
(ii) String from a rubbish bin
(iii) His socks and shoelaces

90 (i) He was a hospital porter
(ii) He was a fashion shop manager
(iii) He was a barman

Question Rating (R4)

91 (i) A British subject
(ii) A priest
(iii) A married man

92 (i) The Royal Regiment of Wales
(ii) The Leicestershire Regiment
(iii) The Artists Rifles Regiment

93 (i) A school for the mentally subnormal
(ii) An approved school
(iii) A military prison

94 (i) Lancaster
(ii) Lincoln
(iii) London

95 (i) Parkinson's disease
(ii) Alzheimer's disease
(iii) Malaria

96 (i) Field was unfit to plead in 1931 but later regained his sanity
   (ii) Field made a confession to a newspaper
   (iii) Field was in prison abroad but returned to the UK in 1933

97 (i) Guilty but insane
   (ii) Guilty
   (iii) Not Guilty

98 (i) Receive the last rites
   (ii) Make an appeal
   (iii) Make a confession

99 (i) An artist's palette
   (ii) An unfinished portrait of her
   (iii) A painter's brush made from human hair

100 (i) His dog
   (ii) His cat
   (iii) His hamster

101 (i) He was a postman
   (ii) He was a van driver
   (iii) He was a milkman

102 (i) In a river
   (ii) In a mineshaft
   (iii) In a well

103 (i) They were searching for a missing foreign tourist
   (ii) They were conducting a training exercise
   (iii) They were taking part in a TV documentary

104 (i) Two
   (ii) Three
   (iii) Five

105 (i) He was a quarryman
   (ii) He was a lorry driver and motor mechanic
   (iii) He was a chicken farmer

106 (i) 'The John Barleycorn'
   (ii) 'The Barn'
   (iii) 'The Royal Oak'

107 (i) Life imprisonment
   (ii) The death penalty
   (iii) Twenty years' imprisonment for manslaughter

108 (i) It was the first murder trial in which photographs were allowed in court
(ii) It was the Old Bailey's first murder trial of the twentieth century
(iii) It was the first time a woman juror had taken part in a murder trial

109 (i) Australia
(ii) Canada
(iii) USA

110 (i) Indecent assault
(ii) Attempted murder
(iii) Rape

111 (i) Execution for those found criminally insane
(ii) That, contrary to normal practice, the murderer ought not to be kept in solitary confinement
(iii) That known sex offenders be kept under stricter control

112 (i) Canada
(ii) Australia
(iii) South Africa

113 (i) She had been a cinema attendant
(ii) She had been a barmaid
(iii) She had been a domestic servant

114 (i) The flagstaff bearing the black flag snapped
(ii) The gas lamps all failed
(iii) The trap door failed to open

115 (i) Theft of hotel property
(ii) Arson
(iii) Unlawfully obtaining credit

116 (i) The Pioneer Corps
(ii) The South Wales Borderers
(iii) The Royal Army Medical Corps

117 (i) Wandsworth Prison
(ii) Norwich Prison
(iii) Strangeways Prison

118 (i) Libel proceedings
(ii) Divorce proceedings
(iii) Proceedings for negligence against his solicitor

119 (i) He was a bank clerk
(ii) He was a policeman
(iii) He was an insurance salesman

120 (i) Germany
(ii) The USA
(iii) Great Britain

Question Rating (R5)

121 (i) The death sentence
(ii) Penal servitude for life
(iii) Confinement for an unspecified period in a hospital for the criminally insane

122 (i) In Hyde Park
(ii) In the cellar beneath the murderer's flat
(iii) In the River Ouse

123 (i) Five years
(ii) Twenty-five years
(iii) Forty years

124 (i) A nurse
(ii) A prostitute
(iii) An accounts clerk

125 (i) Ypres
(ii) Passchendaele
(iii) The Somme

126 (i) A scarf
(ii) A tea towel
(iii) A piece of clothes line

127 (i) He was a policeman
(ii) He was a labourer in a quarry
(iii) He was a lorry driver

128 (i) The victim was smothered in honey and eaten alive by ants
(ii) A blazing torch was rammed down the victim's throat
(iii) Acid was poured into the victim's ear

129 (i) Grey flannel
(ii) Blue serge
(iii) Brown corduroy

130 (i) Bootlaces
(ii) Pieces of tape
(iii) Her hands

131 (i) Guilty of manslaughter
(ii) Guilty of concealing a body from the coroner
(iii) Not guilty

132 (i) A strip of curtain
(ii) Blind cord
(iii) A towel

133 (i) Forensic evidence from the victim's fingernails
(ii) An anonymous telephone call
(iii) The defendant's own confession to a newspaper

134 (i) A table knife
(ii) A machete
(iii) An axe

135 (i) *News of the World*
(ii) *Sunday Graphic*
(iii) *Sunday Pictorial*

136 (i) Severe short-sightedness
(ii) A club foot
(iii) A mutilated hand

137 (i) A woman's stocking
(ii) A man's woollen vest
(iii) A fan belt

138 (i) Syphilis
(ii) Asthma
(iii) Tuberculosis

139 (i) Blackmail
(ii) Falsely obtaining money due to the victim under a court order
(iii) Causing grievous bodily harm

140 (i) Petrol
(ii) A cleaning solution
(iii) Holy water

141 (i) His hands
(ii) A pyjama cord
(iii) A bootlace

142 (i) 'Squinter'
(ii) 'Buxy'
(iii) 'Thunder Thighs'

143 (i) A purse
(ii) A box of face powder
(iii) A pen

144 (i) His hands
(ii) A sash cord
(iii) A silk scarf

145 (i) Three
(ii) Nine
(iii) Fifteen

146 (i) *Daily Sketch*
(ii) *News of the World*
(iii) *Guardian*

147 (i) Theft of jewellery
(ii) Theft of cattle
(iii) Blackmail

148 (i) *Daily Mirror*
(ii) *Daily Sketch*
(iii) *People*

149 (i) He died in an air
raid before the
sentence could be
carried out
(ii) He was freed on
appeal
(iii) He committed
suicide

150 (i) The murder weapon
(a leather belt)
(ii) Obscene
photographs of his
victim
(iii) A note confessing to
his guilt

CHAPTER THREE

CLUES

Question Rating (R1)

1
  (i) It was the first hanging of a woman at Wandsworth Prison
  (ii) It was the first hanging of a woman in Britain for over thirty years
  (iii) It was the last hanging of a woman in Britain

2
  (i) Christopher Craig
  (ii) Derek Bentley
  (iii) Albert Stratton

3
  (i) Ascot
  (ii) Hungerford
  (iii) Sunningdale

4
  (i) The A1
  (ii) The A6
  (iii) The A11

5
  (i) Michael Ryan
  (ii) Peter Carew
  (iii) Mark Lewis

6
  (i) He set fire to it
  (ii) He removed all the finger tips with an axe
  (iii) He soaked it in acid

7
  (i) Mary Cotton
  (ii) Maria Marten
  (iii) Margaret Godlewski

8
  (i) Korean
  (ii) Chinese
  (iii) Malayan

9
  (i) The icing over of the River Thames
  (ii) Lights from 'marsh gas'
  (iii) Fog

10
  (i) To the left
  (ii) To the right
  (iii) It has no grooves

11
  (i) George Cornwell
  (ii) George Ince
  (iii) George Davis

12 (i) After the woman who was the victim's mistress

(ii) After the yacht on which the shooting occurred

(iii) After a villa in which the shooting occurred

13 (i) His testicles

(ii) His feet

(iii) His eyes

14 (i) He was an actor

(ii) He was a racing-car driver

(iii) He was a professional footballer

15 (i) German

(ii) American

(iii) Italian

16 (i) Christopher Craig

(ii) Derek Bentley

(iii) PC Miles himself

17 (i) He was a gamekeeper

(ii) He was a doctor

(iii) He was a policeman

18 (i) 'The Devil's Punchbowl'

(ii) 'Lovers' Leap'

(iii) 'Deadman's Hill'

19 (i) Egyptian

(ii) Moroccan

(iii) Turkish

20 (i) He had been knocked over by a car

(ii) In a fierce struggle with police arresting him

(iii) He had jumped from a roof

21 (i) Cornwall

(ii) Hertfordshire

(iii) Northumberland

22 (i) New Zealander

(ii) American

(iii) British

23 (i) William Hare

(ii) William Hughes

(iii) William Corder

24 (i) She was a night club manageress

(ii) She was an actress

(iii) She was an air hostess

25 (i) He was a soldier

(ii) He was a prison warder

(iii) He was a carpenter

26 (i) Jean Cook

(ii) Valerie Storie

(iii) Vera Ellis

27 (i) American
(ii) Swedish
(iii) Danish

28 (i) Buried in the ground
(ii) Packed in straw in the loft
(iii) Dismembered and packed into a water barrel

29 (i) Robbery
(ii) Blackmail (i.e. a protection racket)
(iii) An insurance fraud

30 (i) Pin marks
(ii) Striation marks
(iii) Ejection marks

Question Rating (R2)

31 (i) 'Blue Max'
(ii) 'Max Million'
(iii) 'Red Max'

32 (i) As a chauffeur
(ii) As a butler
(iii) As a groom

33 (i) They were fired from two different guns
(ii) They were silver plated
(iii) They were dumdum rounds

34 (i) Northamptonshire
(ii) Essex
(iii) Devon

35 (i) On a London underground train
(ii) On a London bus
(iii) On a Blackpool tram

36 (i) British
(ii) French
(iii) Belgian

37 (i) Brentwood, Essex
(ii) Staines, Middlesex
(iii) Croydon, Surrey

38 (i) Cartridge cases from the murder weapon
(ii) The victim's watch
(iii) A handwritten confession

39 (i) A revolver with a silencer
(ii) A flare pistol
(iii) A sawn-off shotgun

40 (i) He was a railway ticket collector
(ii) He was a policeman
(iii) He was a newspaper reporter

41 (i) Yorkshire
(ii) Cumbria
(iii) Lancashire

42
(i) He was hit accidentally by a stray bullet
(ii) He was shot dead by the police
(iii) He was shot while trying to foil the escape of a number of robbers

43
(i) Australia
(ii) Canada
(iii) USA

44
(i) He was a soldier
(ii) He was a schoolteacher
(iii) He was a portrait painter

45
(i) A London Transport bus
(ii) A horse and cart
(iii) A motor cycle

46
(i) 'The Cleft Chin Murder'
(ii) 'The Green Eyes Murder'
(iii) 'The Hare Lip Murder'

47
(i) He was a gamekeeper
(ii) He was a professional burglar
(iii) He was a policeman

48
(i) In a well
(ii) In a stable
(iii) In a drainage ditch

49
(i) He was found to be insane and unfit to plead
(ii) He committed suicide
(iii) He escaped from custody and disappeared

50
(i) On a passenger liner
(ii) On a railway train
(iii) In a motor car

51
(i) He was a tobacconist
(ii) He was a greengrocer
(iii) He was a tailor

52
(i) They were cousins
(ii) They were friends and business partners
(iii) They were lovers

53
(i) He was recognized as a former policeman
(ii) He was recognized as a known robber
(iii) He was recognized from an Identikit picture

54 (i) Cheshire
(ii) Essex
(iii) Warwickshire

55 (i) Polstead, Suffolk
(ii) Pangbourne, Berkshire
(iii) Plymouth, Devon

56 (i) The gas spectrometer
(ii) The paraffin analyser
(iii) The comparison microscope

57 (i) Sussex
(ii) Surrey
(iii) Essex

58 (i) Essex
(ii) Kent
(iii) Sussex

59 (i) They were poaching deer
(ii) They were in a stolen car
(iii) They were forging bank notes

60 (i) Russian
(ii) Czechoslovak
(iii) Polish

Question Rating (R3)

61 (i) A stiff right leg
(ii) Icy blue eyes
(iii) Blonde eyebrows

62 (i) Yorkshire
(ii) Devon
(iii) Lincolnshire

63 (i) Fifteen and eighteen
(ii) Sixteen and nineteen
(iii) Seventeen and twenty

64 (i) She was a nurse
(ii) She was a striptease dancer
(iii) She was a housewife

65 (i) He wanted to delay recognition until he made good his escape from the country
(ii) He wanted to fake his own suicide
(iii) He wanted to make it appear to be the accidental death of a vagrant

66 (i) He was a church warden
(ii) He was a confectioner
(iii) He was a policeman

67 (i) A thunderstorm
(ii) Fog and mist
(iii) Heavy snow

68 (i) A bolt of lightning struck the Red Barn, revealing some clothing
(ii) The area was flooded and on receding the water was stained red with blood
(iii) The victim's mother had a dream about the location of the body

69 (i) Blackpool
(ii) Rhyl
(iii) Swansea

70 (i) A shotgun
(ii) A pistol
(iii) A blunderbuss

71 (i) He was a schoolteacher
(ii) He was a bank clerk
(iii) He was a research scientist

72 (i) Aberdeen
(ii) Edinburgh
(iii) Glasgow

73 (i) The Royal Engineers
(ii) The Coldstream Guards
(iii) The Royal Hussars

74 (i) A Smith and Wesson
(ii) A Browning
(iii) A Derringer

75 (i) She was an actress
(ii) She was a nurse
(iii) She was a housekeeper

76 (i) Great Britain
(ii) Canada
(iii) Germany

77 (i) Lee Enfield
(ii) Thompson
(iii) Webley

78 (i) Lloyds Bank
(ii) Barclays Bank
(iii) National Westminster Bank

79 (i) He was a naval reserve officer
(ii) He was an army chaplain
(iii) He was a deserter from the army

80 (i) Bare knuckle prizefighting
(ii) A bank robbery
(iii) A bookmaking deal

81 (i) Lieutenant
(ii) Captain
(iii) Major

82 (i) A jeweller's shop
(ii) An antique shop
(iii) A tobacconist's shop

83 (i) 'Tam'
(ii) 'Jock'
(iii) 'Scottie'

84 (i) Essex
(ii) Surrey
(iii) Hertfordshire

85 (i) An army truck
(ii) A motor cycle and sidecar
(iii) A rowing boat

86 (i) Sussex
(ii) Kent
(iii) Surrey

87 (i) Her brother's
(ii) Her father's
(iii) Her husband's

88 (i) He was a builder
(ii) He was a coal merchant
(iii) He was a publican

89 (i) In an armchair in the bedroom
(ii) In a bath in the kitchen
(iii) In a trunk in the living room

90 (i) That they were lovers
(ii) That they were father and son
(iii) That they were half-brothers

Question Rating (R4)

91 (i) He was an insurance loss adjuster
(ii) He was an auctioneer and surveyor
(iii) He was a publican

92 (i) He said that she had committed suicide with the gun
(ii) He said that she had examined the gun and discharged it accidentally
(iii) He said that she had fired the gun at him and had been killed by a 'ricocheting' bullet

93 (i) A car
(ii) A London bus
(iii) A milk lorry

94 (i) They were
policemen

(ii) They were security
guards

(iii) They were bank
cashiers

95 (i) Eton College

(ii) Rugby School

(iii) Harrow School

96 (i) He was a garage
mechanic

(ii) He was a farmer

(iii) He was a travelling
salesman

97 (i) He was a cook in a
hotel

(ii) He was a builder's
labourer

(iii) He was a dock
worker

98 (i) He was making a
blackmail telephone
call which was
traced by the police

(ii) He was making an
obscene telephone
call, overheard by a
passer-by

(iii) He was damaging
the telephone box in
a fit of temper

99 (i) A brewing firm

(ii) A colliery

(iii) A bank

100 (i) In the victim's
notebook

(ii) In the telephone
book

(iii) On a receipt for the
purchase of a gun

101 (i) Wiltshire

(ii) Hampshire

(iii) Shropshire

102 (i) Because Dyer had
fled the country and
was never heard of
again

(ii) Because Dyer was
already dead by
then

(iii) Because it was not
possible to show
that Tombe's death
had occurred within
the legal time limit

103 (i) Britain's first
introduction agency

(ii) Britain's first private
detective firm

(iii) Britain's first
department store

104 (i) A blunderbuss

(ii) A shotgun

(iii) A revolver

105 (i) A dairy
(ii) A bank
(iii) A building society

106 (i) Alcatraz
(ii) Devil's Island
(iii) Dartmoor

107 (i) About two years
(ii) About four years
(iii) Over ten years

108 (i) Two
(ii) Three
(iii) Five

109 (i) The London Docks
(ii) Waterloo Station
(iii) The Albert Hall

110 (i) 'The Invisible Man'
(ii) 'The Green Man'
(iii) 'The Hooded Man'

111 (i) The victim's mother had a dream which accurately located the body of her dead son
(ii) A professional clairvoyant found the body
(iii) The body was found by a dog burying some bones

112 (i) Southend-on-Sea, Essex

(ii) Brighton, Sussex
(iii) Ramsgate, Kent

113 (i) That she had a new lover
(ii) That she had a venereal disease
(iii) That she was pregnant

114 (i) Both witnesses failed to identify him on an identity parade
(ii) Both witnesses were also shot dead by him
(iii) Both witnesses were too frightened to attend an identity parade

115 (i) They were landlord and tenant
(ii) They were employer and employee
(iii) They were business partners

116 (i) An informer's evidence
(ii) Circumstantial evidence
(iii) Hearsay evidence

117 (i) A green cravat
(ii) White gloves
(iii) A wide-brimmed hat

118 (i) He was declared
bankrupt
(ii) His head was
severely injured in a
fight
(iii) He contracted
syphilis

119 (i) Mrs Muriel Maynard
at the 'Hole in the
Wall Restaurant'
(ii) Mrs Muriel McKay at
the 'Wishing Well
Restaurant'
(iii) Mrs Muriel Patience
at the 'Barn
Restaurant'

120 (i) Derham was in love
with Smith's wife
(ii) Derham was
blackmailing Smith,
who was a deserter
from the army
(iii) Smith had removed
Derham from his will
after he discovered
a fraudulent
business deal

Question Rating (R5)

121 (i) He was in prison
(ii) He was in the Royal
Navy

(iii) He was in the
French Foreign
Legion

122 (i) They were both
deserters
(ii) They were both
fighter pilots
(iii) They were both
military attachés at
the Soviet Embassy

123 (i) He had been a
policeman
(ii) He had been a
veterinary surgeon
(iii) He had been a
dentist

124 (i) A Luger
(ii) A Smith and
Wesson
(iii) A Berreta

125 (i) Cambridgeshire
(ii) Lincolnshire
(iii) Norfolk

126 (i) France
(ii) Germany
(iii) USA

127 (i) He was a motor-
cycle repair shop
owner
(ii) He was a
blacksmith
(iii) He was an antique
dealer

128 (i) At his farm
(ii) At a local hospital
(iii) At a local cinema

129 (i) He was an architect
(ii) He was a brewer
(iii) He was an accountant

130 (i) Warwickshire
(ii) Cambridgeshire
(iii) Cheshire

131 (i) He was a milkman
(ii) He was a gardener
(iii) He was a painter

132 (i) 'Habeas Corpus'
(ii) A 'health order'
(iii) A 'repression order'

133 (i) Cobb posed as a criminal and offered to buy the murder weapon from Orrock
(ii) Cobb prised some bullets from a tree, which had been used by the murderer for 'practice' shots, for ballistic comparison
(iii) Cobb persuaded Orrock to make a statement which contained certain facts known only to the murderer

134 (i) There were three bullet wounds in her back
(ii) The bullets had been fired from long range
(iii) The suicide notes were written after her death

135 (i) 'Red Ruben'
(ii) 'Russian Robert'
(iii) 'The Red Tsar'

136 (i) Clarke was tricked into retrieving the murder weapon from its hiding place by a police informant
(ii) A bullet, previously fired from a gun by Clarke was removed from the ceiling of a house and found to match the murder bullets
(iii) The murder weapon was found in a river by chance during a routine police training exercise

137 (i) He was in the
Merchant Navy
(ii) He was in the Army
(iii) He was in the
Colonial Service in
India

138 (i) A sweet shop
(ii) A chapel
(iii) A funeral parlour

139 (i) He was a sailor
(ii) He was a cook
(iii) He was a journalist

140 (i) Organizing a
'protection racket' at
night clubs
(ii) Arranging marriage
ceremonies for
women wanting
British citizenship
(iii) Running a brothel

141 (i) 'Moat Farm'
(ii) 'The Grange'
(iii) 'The Welcomes'

142 (i) Yorkshire
(ii) Lancashire
(iii) Northumberland

143 (i) A shotgun
(ii) A hunting rifle
(iii) A revolver

144 (i) Henry Poole
(ii) George MacKay
(iii) Edmund Stevens

145 (i) A Browning
(ii) A Luger
(iii) A Webley

146 (i) One
(ii) Two
(iii) Five

147 (i) They were
gamekeepers
(ii) They were
policemen
(iii) They were farm
labourers

148 (i) A Browning
(ii) A Luger
(iii) A Webley

149 (i) Nantwich, Cheshire
(ii) Skegness,
Lincolnshire
(iii) Margate, Kent

150 (i) He was a labourer
(ii) He was a
gamekeeper
(iii) He was a poultry
farmer

CHAPTER FOUR

CLUES

Question Rating (R1)

1
  (i) Brian Epstein
  (ii) Janis Joplin
  (iii) Joe Orton

2
  (i) Leeds
  (ii) Liverpool
  (iii) London

3
  (i) On Clapham Common
  (ii) In Hyde Park
  (iii) In Regent's Park

4
  (i) He was Austrian
  (ii) He was German
  (iii) He was Swiss

5
  (i) 'Murder by persons unknown'
  (ii) 'Murder by Lord Lucan'
  (iii) 'Murder most foul'

6
  (i) He was a travelling salesman
  (ii) He was a bank cashier
  (iii) He was an insurance agent

7
  (i) London
  (ii) Birmingham
  (iii) Glasgow

8
  (i) German
  (ii) Italian
  (iii) Russian

9
  (i) A hospital
  (ii) A theatre
  (iii) A hotel

10
  (i) He was a dairy cattle stockman
  (ii) He was a shepherd
  (iii) He was a chicken farmer

11
  (i) Prudential Assurance
  (ii) Marks & Spencer
  (iii) Lloyds of London

12 (i)   He had
              dismembered her
              body
       (ii) He had thrown her
              body into a vat of
              acid
       (iii) He had plastered
              her body into the
              wall of the building

13 (i)   'Bill', because she
              was a lesbian
       (ii) 'Bess', because she
              believed herself to
              be the reincarnation
              of Queen Elizabeth I
       (iii) 'Bridey', because
              she was Irish

14 (i)   Birmingham
       (ii) London
       (iii) Leeds

15 (i)   She was a lady's
              maid
       (ii) She was a dress
              shop owner
       (iii) She was a prostitute

16 (i)   A cloakroom ticket
       (ii) A love letter
       (iii) A pawnbroker's
              receipt for a ring

17 (i)   Edinburgh
       (ii) Leeds
       (iii) London

18 (i)   'Biffo' Manton
       (ii) 'Barney' Manton
       (iii) 'Bertie' Manton

19 (i)   Melbourne,
              Australia
       (ii) New York, USA
       (iii) Durban, South
              Africa

20 (i)   A rattle
       (ii) A glove puppet
       (iii) A lantern

21 (i)   In a lighthouse
       (ii) In a rented
              bungalow
       (iii) In a railway shed

22 (i)   Essex
       (ii) Sussex
       (iii) Hertfordshire

23 (i)   He was Irish
       (ii) He was German
       (iii) He was Russian

24 (i)   Inside a sack
       (ii) Inside a ballgown
       (iii) Inside a mattress

25 (i) A shape like the 'Star of David' was cut into the left cheek

(ii) A shape like the letter 'S' was cut into each cheek

(iii) A shape like the letter 'V' was cut into each ear lobe

26 (i) Rudyard Kipling

(ii) Sir Arthur Conan Doyle

(iii) George Bernard Shaw

27 (i) London

(ii) Southampton

(iii) Liverpool

28 (i) She was a children's nanny

(ii) She was a cook

(iii) She was a maid

29 (i) The first murder in a museum

(ii) The first murder in a music hall

(iii) The first murder on a train

30 (i) He was a newspaper vendor

(ii) He was a pantry boy

(iii) He was a hospital porter

Question Rating (R2)

31 (i) His pregnant wife, Ruby

(ii) His disabled sister, Joan

(iii) His mother, Ethel

32 (i) Cambridge

(ii) Oxford

(iii) Exeter

33 (i) A night club

(ii) A boys' club

(iii) A chess club

34 (i) Major

(ii) Captain

(iii) Colonel

35 (i) A pawnbroker's shop in Holborn, London

(ii) Waterloo Station, London

(iii) Dover Docks, Kent

36 (i) Eighteen years old

(ii) Sixty-three years old

(iii) It is not known for certain

37 (i) In a river

(ii) In a garden shed

(iii) In a public park

38 (i) Robbery
(ii) Silencing a police informer
(iii) The inheritance of property in a will

39 (i) She always wore black
(ii) She always wore one particular green hat
(iii) She dressed in men's clothing

40 (i) On the seashore
(ii) The lock of a canal
(iii) On a refuse tip

41 (i) France
(ii) Ireland
(iii) USA

42 (i) He was a jeweller
(ii) He was an actor
(iii) He was a landlord

43 (i) A grain warehouse
(ii) A railway left luggage office
(iii) An oil company depot

44 (i) Bexhill-on-Sea
(ii) Blackpool
(iii) Bournemouth

45 (i) Robbery from a safe

(ii) Jealousy. The murderer was the victim's wife's lover
(iii) Revenge. The victim had formerly mistreated the murderer's mother

46 (i) A type of hat
(ii) A type of shoe
(iii) A type of cravat

47 (i) 'The Mumbles'
(ii) 'The Crumbles'
(iii) 'The Tumbles'

48 (i) Cocaine
(ii) Marijuana
(iii) Morphia

49 (i) He said that she had committed suicide with poison
(ii) He said that she had accidentally hit her head on a coal scuttle during a fight with him
(iii) He said that she had been stabbed by intruders while he was out fishing

50 (i) She was a typist
(ii) She was a barmaid
(iii) She was a children's nanny

51 (i) London
(ii) Liverpool
(iii) Southampton

52 (i) A hair brush
(ii) A rolling pin
(iii) A walking stick

53 (i) He had been an insurance agent
(ii) He had been a salesman
(iii) He had been a motor mechanic

54 (i) He was an ambulance driver
(ii) He was a driver for the National Fire Service
(iii) He was a train driver

55 (i) The Isle of Arran
(ii) The Isle of Anglesey
(iii) The Isle of Man

56 (i) He was a kosher butcher
(ii) He was a hairdresser
(iii) He was a tailor

57 (i) A nursing home
(ii) A public house
(iii) A prison

58 (i) A walking stick
(ii) A billiard cue
(iii) A police truncheon

59 (i) In Scotland
(ii) In Canada
(iii) In India

60 (i) They were discovered, by the victim, burying a corpse
(ii) They were discovered, by the victim, during a burglary
(iii) They were discovered, by the victim, taking lead from the roof

Question Rating (R3)

61 (i) The Royal Flying Corps
(ii) The Royal Navy
(iii) The Machine-Gun Corps

62 (i) He was an insurance salesman
(ii) He was a ladies' lingerie salesman
(iii) He was a soda fountain salesman

63 (i) An axe
(ii) A hammer
(iii) A poker

64 (i) 'The Bedfordshire Bundle'
(ii) 'The Sandy Mystery'
(iii) 'The Luton Sack Murder'

65 (i) She was an unemployed nurse
(ii) She was an unemployed maid
(iii) She was an unemployed typist

66 (i) He was a professional prizefighter
(ii) He was a professional burglar
(iii) He was a professional circus strongman

67 (i) 'Greaser'
(ii) 'Wag'
(iii) 'Pigsticker'

68 (i) A Palace of Varieties
(ii) A church
(iii) A museum

69 (i) They were blacksmiths
(ii) They were casual labourers
(iii) They were lightermen

70 (i) He wanted to carry out the 'perfect murder'
(ii) He wanted to avoid marriage to his victim
(iii) He wanted to avoid paying her money he owed

71 (i) He was an apprentice painter
(ii) He was a tarpaulin packer
(iii) He was a sail maker

72 (i) A revolver
(ii) A jemmy
(iii) An axe

73 (i) As a chauffeur/handyman
(ii) As a bookbinder
(iii) As a stockman

74 (i) A cook's knife and a meat saw
(ii) A revolver and some rope
(iii) Rubber gloves and a torch

75 (i) A railway carriage
(ii) A refuse tip
(iii) A barge

76 (i) She was a
        shorthand typist and
        bookkeeper
   (ii) She was a cook
   (iii) She was an actress
        and model

77 (i) A hammer
   (ii) A tyre lever
   (iii) A billiard ball in a
        sock

78 (i) She had been a bus
        conductress
   (ii) She had been in the
        Royal Air Force
   (ii) She had been a
        War Reserve
        Policewoman

79 (i) The beam was
        proved to be too frail
        to have supported
        her weight
   (ii) The beam was
        proved to have been
        too high for suicide
        to have been
        accomplished
   (iii) The beam showed
        no marks from the
        cord supposedly
        used

80 (i) 'Moosh' and 'Tiggy'
   (ii) 'Cain' and 'Abel'
   (iii) 'Smiler' and 'Crash'

81 (i) Lincolnshire
   (ii) Lancashire
   (iii) Leicestershire

82 (i) He had beaten her,
        then pushed her
        from a tower block
   (ii) He had beaten her
        to death with the
        branch of a tree
   (iii) He had driven over
        her, repeatedly, with
        a car

83 (i) He was a taxi driver
   (ii) He was a post office
        clerk
   (iii) He was a policeman

84 (i) He was an Egyptian
   (ii) He was a Turkish
        Cypriot
   (iii) He was an Indian

85 (i) They were sisters
   (ii) They were one and
        the same person
   (iii) They were mother
        and daughter

86 (i) Somerset
   (ii) Surrey
   (iii) Sussex

87 (i) With his bare hands
   (ii) With a golf club
   (iii) With a wooden stool

88 (i) A horse and cart
(ii) A bicycle
(iii) A handcart

89 (i) A torch
(ii) A spanner
(iii) A car jack

90 (i) He was a probation officer
(ii) He was a police officer
(iii) He was a prison officer

Question Rating (R4)

91 (i) Yorkshire
(ii) Derbyshire
(iii) Nottinghamshire

92 (i) His second wife
(ii) An eye witness
(iii) A priest

93 (i) He was a surgeon
(ii) He was an architect
(iii) He was a barrister

94 (i) His fingerprints
(ii) His photograph
(iii) His visiting card

95 (i) A tobacconist's shop
(ii) A grocer's shop
(iii) A pawnbroker's shop

96 (i) He was a solicitor
(ii) He was a policeman
(iii) He was a sailor

97 (i) Lancashire
(ii) Wiltshire
(iii) Yorkshire

98 (i) Cardiff
(ii) Edinburgh
(iii) Manchester

99 (i) A blow across the heart (possibly from an Indian club)
(ii) A blow across the throat (possibly a karate chop)
(iii) A blow across the nose (possibly from a whip)

100 (i) The cinema
(ii) Newspapers' sensationalism
(iii) Glue sniffing

101 (i) She was French
(ii) She was Belgian
(iii) She was Canadian

102 (i) He was a headmaster
(ii) He was a solicitor
(iii) He was a bank manager

103 (i) White silk
   (ii) Black satin
   (iii) Red corduroy

104 (i) An oar
   (ii) A shovel
   (iii) An axe

105 (i) In a church
   (ii) In a farmhouse
   (iii) In a shop

106 (i) A hammer
   (ii) An Indian club
   (iii) A kitchen stool

107 (i) On a railway train bound for Scotland
   (ii) In police custody for another offence
   (iii) In a church attending Mass

108 (i) His mis-spelling of a word which matched a similar mis-spelling in letters he purported to have received from his wife, but which were dated after her death

   (ii) His saliva was found on a cigarette end in the clothing of the victim and matched against that on envelopes he had used to send letters to the police

   (iii) The evidence of a newspaper boy which completely destroyed Manton's alibi evidence

109 (i) A solid silver statuette
   (ii) A cricket bat
   (iii) A hammer

110 (i) He had been a boxer
   (ii) He had been a professional footballer
   (iii) He had been a karate champion

111 (i) A bowler hat
   (ii) A velvet jacket
   (iii) A leather shoe

112 (i) The victim had stolen food from them
(ii) The victim had goaded them on account of their homosexual relationship
(iii) The victim had attempted to blackmail them over a previous robbery

113 (i) In a wheelbarrow
(ii) On his bicycle
(iii) In his car

114 (i) He was a train driver
(ii) He was a motor mechanic
(iii) He was a refuse collector

115 (i) Lincolnshire
(ii) Oxfordshire
(iii) Cambridgeshire

116 (i) He was a fish porter
(ii) He was a soldier
(iii) He was a knife grinder

117 (i) The drug, cocaine
(ii) Mrs Alma Rattenbury, the victim's wife
(iii) Witchcraft

118 (i) The victim was blackmailing the murderer
(ii) The victim was having a homosexual affair with the murderer
(iii) The victim had discovered that the murderer was committing fraud

119 (i) Her gloves
(ii) Her boots
(iii) Her earrings

120 (i) In an air raid shelter
(ii) In a boathouse
(iii) In a mineshaft

Question Rating (R5)

121 (i) Dr Crippen
(ii) Patrick Mahon
(iii) Henry Wainewright

122 (i) 'One minute Michaelson'
(ii) 'Magic Michaelson'
(iii) 'Made in a moment Michaelson'

123 (i) He was a jockey
(ii) He was a professional boxer
(iii) He was a tennis coach

124 (i) A rolling pin
(ii) A tubular steel chair
(iii) A paperweight

125 (i) Not proven
(ii) Guilty of manslaughter (not guilty of murder)
(iii) Guilty but insane

126 (i) She had been left with her head lying in a gas oven
(ii) She had been hanged by her neck from a curtain rail
(iii) She had been pushed from her bedroom window

127 (i) A candlestick telephone
(ii) A mallet
(iii) A solid silver statuette

128 (i) Northumbria
(ii) Staffordshire
(iii) Cornwall

129 (i) She was pretending to be her victim's long ago adopted daughter returned from Australia

(ii) She was pretending to her husband that she was at her sister's house 'in confinement', prior to having a baby
(iii) She was pretending to be in hiding from a lover who was trying to kill her

130 (i) They were circus clowns
(ii) They were elephant keepers
(iii) They were professoinal 'fire eaters'

131 (i) A steam iron
(ii) A poker
(iii) A rolling pin

132 (i) He claimed she had committed suicide
(ii) He claimed that he was defending himself from a knife attack
(iii) He claimed it was a road traffic accident

133 (i) As a chauffeur
(ii) As a butler
(iii) As a cook

134 (i) Yorkshire
(ii) Devon
(iii) Cumbria

135 (i) An iron carpet rod
(ii) An iron golf tee
marker
(iii) A shovel

136 (i) He was a lorry
driver
(ii) He was a farmer
(iii) He was a painter
and decorator

137 (i) On a mountain
(ii) In a lake
(iii) In a pot hole

138 (i) A fingerprint
(ii) A footprint
(iii) A palm print

139 (i) As a cook
(ii) As a children's
nanny
(iii) As a travelling
companion

140 (i) A paperweight
(ii) A flat iron
(iii) The lead weight
from a sash window

141 (i) Paris
(ii) Liverpool
(iii) New York

142 (i) 'Quentin'
(ii) 'Qualtrough'
(iii) 'Quillion'

143 (i) Fifteen years old
(ii) Seventy years old
(iii) Fifty-five years old

144 (i) A car jack
(ii) A hammer
(iii) A gold statuette

145 (i) 39 Hilldrop Crescent
West, Chapletown
(ii) 84 Knapp Road,
Bow, London
(iii) 25 Menlove
Gardens East,
Mossley Hill

146 (i) A pistol
(ii) A pair of scales
(iii) A house brick

147 (i) He said it was a
road accident, with
the car hitting a tree
(ii) He said it was a
case of suicide, with
his wife jumping
from the moving car
(iii) He said that his wife
had been struck by
a 'hit and run' driver
as they were
changing a tyre

148 (i) In a lorry
     (ii) In a pram
     (iii) In a wheelbarrow

149 (i) On a golf course
     (ii) In a mineshaft
     (iii) In a zoo

150 (i) Leibowitz
     (ii) Leschziner
     (iii) Lurgen

CHAPTER FIVE

CLUES

Question Rating (R1)

1
   (i) He was a fireman
   (ii) He was a press photographer
   (iii) He was a policeman

2
   (i) About one half
   (ii) About one quarter
   (iii) The majority

3
   (i) Oscar Wilde
   (ii) Kevin Barry
   (iii) George Bernard Shaw

4
   (i) Closed wounds and open wounds
   (ii) Incised wounds and stab wounds
   (iii) Upper body wounds and lower body wounds

5
   (i) Computer enhancement of photographs

   (ii) The voiceprint
   (iii) The Identikit system

6
   (i) He was Swiss
   (ii) He was French
   (iii) He was Belgian

7
   (i) Devon
   (ii) Durham
   (iii) Derbyshire

8
   (i) John du Rose
   (ii) Jack Capstick
   (iii) Robert Fabian

9
   (i) He was an executioner
   (ii) He was a prison warder
   (iii) He was a soldier

10
   (i) The Broadwater Farm Estate
   (ii) The Stonehaven Estate
   (iii) The Notting Hill Estate

11 (i) The House of Lords
   (ii) The English Synod
   (iii) The Court of the Star Chamber

12 (i) They were cousins
   (ii) They were employer and employee
   (iii) They were homosexual lovers

13 (i) American
   (ii) Australian
   (iii) South African

14 (i) Painting
   (ii) Writing
   (iii) Music

15 (i) They formed a 'Defence Committee' for the convicted man
   (ii) They formed a 'vigilante' group to patrol the village
   (iii) They formed a committee to lobby Parliament for the re-introduction of the death penalty

16 (i) Glasgow
   (ii) Edinburgh
   (iii) Aberdeen

17 (i) She was a barmaid
   (ii) She was a member of the Salvation Army
   (iii) She was a prostitute

18 (i) Gloucestershire
   (ii) Herefordshire
   (iii) Cheshire

19 (i) He was Italian
   (ii) He was Indian
   (iii) He was Turkish

20 (i) He was arrested on his return, to England, from transportation to Van Diemen's Land
   (ii) He gave himself up to the police and confessed
   (iii) He was 'informed on' by his son

21 (i) He was a horse trader
   (ii) He was a Hackney carriage driver
   (iii) He was an actor

22 (i) Somerset
   (ii) Kent
   (iii) Lancashire

23 (i) He was an actor
   (ii) He was a pawnbroker
   (iii) He was a tailor

24 (i) His wife
(ii) His brother
(iii) His daughter

25 (i) The Royal Air Force
(ii) The Royal Navy
(iii) The Army

26 (i) It had been hit by an ocean liner
(ii) It had been thrown from an aircraft
(iii) It had been thrown from a train

27 (i) He was a bouncer in a club
(ii) He was a police officer
(iii) He was a professional boxer

28 (i) Percy Thompson, his lover's husband
(ii) Percy le Neve, his lover's brother
(iii) Percy Major, his lover's father

29 (i) John O'Groats
(ii) Gretna Green
(iii) Coldstream

30 (i) 'The Mother Red Cap'
(ii) 'The Rising Sun'
(iii) 'The Five Bells'

Question Rating (R2)

31 (i) Ethel le Neve
(ii) Edith Major
(iii) Edith Thompson

32 (i) To have sexual intercourse
(ii) To collect a prescription for drugs
(iii) To purchase antiques

33 (i) Aleistair Crowley
(ii) No one was ever convicted
(iii) Neville Heath

34 (i) Richard Williams
(ii) Robert Wood
(iii) Raymond White

35 (i) He was a milkman
(ii) He was a bus conductor
(iii) He was a taxi driver

36 (i) A will specifically excluding the victim from his estate
(ii) A fictional crime story which contained details of the real murder
(iii) A suicide note

37 (i) Following his
release in 1958 he
made a confession,
published in a
newspaper
(ii) He made a 'death
bed' confession to
the prison chaplain
(iii) A twenty-year-old
written confession
was found among
his effects after he
died

38 (i) He was a
Presbyterian
minister
(ii) He was an actor
(iii) He was a merchant
seaman

39 (i) A butcher's shop
(ii) An antique shop
(iii) A dress shop

40 (i) Financial – the
murderer stood to
benefit under the
victim's will
(ii) Jealousy – the
murderer was
having an affair with
the victim's husband
(iii) Revenge – the
victim had assaulted
the murderer's child

41 (i) He was a labourer
(ii) He was a policeman
(iii) He was a sailor

42 (i) York
(ii) London
(iii) Bristol

43 (i) She was a
chambermaid
(ii) She was a prostitute
(iii) She was a hotel
manager

44 (i) *Men Only* magazine
(ii) *Playboy* magazine
(iii) *Mayfair* magazine

45 (i) He was a Spaniard
(ii) He was Italian
(iii) He was Libyan

46 (i) Devon
(ii) Essex
(iii) Norfolk

47 (i) She was a barmaid
(ii) She was a prostitute
(iii) She was a secretary

48 (i) John Williams
(ii) John Lee
(iii) John Smith

49 (i) Derbyshire
(ii) Essex
(iii) Hampshire

50 (i) Jealousy – she was having an affair with a man at a nearby love-nest
(ii) Revenge – she had poisoned his dog
(iii) Greed – she was about to change her will

51 (i) 'Nicky the Greek'
(ii) 'The Blade'
(iii) 'Big X'

52 (i) Surrey
(ii) Hertfordshire
(iii) Kent

53 (i) Three
(ii) None
(iii) Five

54 (i) Staffordshire
(ii) Devon
(iii) Hampshire

55 (i) None
(ii) One
(iii) Four

56 (i) The anti-blood sports movement
(ii) The anti-nuclear movement
(iii) The anti-Fascist movement

57 (i) A railway carriage
(ii) A fun fair
(iii) An art gallery

58 (i) The Royal Navy
(ii) The Army (Royal Engineers)
(iii) The Royal Air Force

59 (i) Essex
(ii) Hertfordshire
(iii) Kent

60 (i) Because the defendant was drunk and believed his victim to be a dummy
(ii) Because the defendant was educationally sub-normal and could not form the necessary intent
(iii) Because the defendant was suffering from 'shell shock' after the War

Question Rating (R3)

61 (i) Wales
(ii) Scotland
(iii) The Channel Islands

62 (i) Dismemberment of one who has disgraced their family then sending the parts on trains heading in different directions

(ii) Dismemberment of one who has committed adultery and feeding of the body parts to pigs

(iii) Dismemberment of one who has committed murder then sending the body parts to the aggrieved family

63 (i) Able Seaman
(ii) Flight Lieutenant
(iii) Gunner

64 (i) USA
(ii) Australia
(iii) Eire

65 (i) One of the Appeal Court Judges concerned told a newspaper that he had doubts about the safety of the conviction

(ii) Another man confessed to the earlier killing

(iii) A clairvoyant named another suspect as the true killer

66 (i) The White Star Line
(ii) The P & O Line
(iii) The Cunard Line

67 (i) She was American
(ii) She was Irish
(iii) She was Australian

68 (i) Screened advertisements in cinemas
(ii) BBC radio broadcasts
(iii) BBC television broadcasts

69 (i) With a letter opener
(ii) With a Japanese samurai sword
(iii) With a screwdriver

70 (i) Cancer
(ii) Diphtheria
(iii) Tuberculosis

71 (i) He was a stockbroker
(ii) He was a landlord
(iii) He was a solicitor

72 (i) Clywd
(ii) Powys
(iii) Cumbria

73 (i) He was dead from natural causes
    (ii) He was certified criminally insane
    (iii) He was extradited to the USA for a previous murder

74 (i) He had been a railway engine driver
    (ii) He had been a blacksmith
    (iii) He had been a hospital orderly

75 (i) He was Israeli
    (ii) He was Australian
    (iii) He was a Barbadian

76 (i) She was a children's nanny
    (ii) She was a prostitute
    (iii) She was a flower seller

77 (i) He was the doctor who performed the post-mortem examination on the murderer's body
    (ii) He was the undertaker who buried the murderer's corpse
    (iii) He was the hangman's assistant at the murderer's execution

78 (i) Mrs Cynthia Payne
    (ii) Mrs Cynthia Jarrett
    (iii) Mrs Mabel Norman

79 (i) Stockport, Cheshire
    (ii) Bootle, Lancashire
    (iii) Workington, Cumbria

80 (i) None
    (ii) Three
    (iii) Six

81 (i) Northolt
    (ii) Ilford
    (iii) Wimbledon

82 (i) He gave himself up to the police
    (ii) He was handed over to the police by a priest to whom he had gone for advice
    (iii) He was identified by DNA profiling

83 (i) Surrey
    (ii) Lancashire
    (iii) Worcestershire

84 (i) He was a butler
    (ii) He was a gardener
    (iii) He was a publican

85 (i) At Madame
Tussaud's
waxworks
(ii) In Hyde Park
(iii) On Dartford Heath

86 (i) The Devil's Dyke
(ii) The Devil's Elbow
(iii) The Devil's
Punchbowl

87 (i) He was the victim's
lover
(ii) He was having a
homosexual affair
with a hotel worker
(iii) He was a builder
working on repairs
at the hotel

88 (i) It was a superstition
that the corpse
would bleed when
touched by its killer
(ii) It was a superstition
that the eyes of a
corpse would flicker
when touched by its
killer
(iii) It was a legal
requirement that the
accused be allowed
to swear his guilt or
innocence 'on the
body' of the victim

89 (i) The Army
(ii) The Navy
(iii) The Air Force

90 (i) An SS dagger
(ii) A hay fork
(iii) A crucifix

Question Rating (R4)

91 (i) 'Smiler'
(ii) 'Whistler'
(iii) 'Wag'

92 (i) He was taking
pornographic
pictures of children
(ii) He was smuggling
drugs
(iii) He was running a
brothel

93 (i) He drank the
victim's blood
(ii) The victim was
apparently still alive
at the time
(iii) It was carried out in
an abattoir

94 (i) A bayonet
(ii) A table knife
(iii) A commando knife

95 (i) A dance-hall
(ii) A cinema
(iii) A public house

96 (i) She was an antique
dealer
(ii) She was a prostitute
(iii) She was a doctor

97 (i) A public house
(ii) A brothel
(iii) A stable

98 (i) They were
fishermen
(ii) They were dairymen
(iii) They were
coalminers

99 (i) Lancaster
(ii) York
(iii) Manchester

100 (i) He was a
highwayman
(ii) He was a sailor
(iii) He was a turnpike
keeper

101 (i) India
(ii) Ireland
(iii) Austria

102 (i) Leeds
(ii) Manchester
(iii) Sheffield

103 (i) He was Canadian
(ii) He was Italian
(iii) He was French

104 (i) Stepney
(ii) Camberwell
(iii) Hendon

105 (i) A brewery and a
hotel
(ii) A mill and a building
contractor's
business
(iii) A local newspaper
and a publisher's
business

106 (i) Twenty-four hours
(ii) Forty years
(iii) Twenty-four years

107 (i) For being an
accessory to the
crime
(ii) For concealing a
body from the
coroner
(iii) For forgery

108 (i) Not guilty, a case of
mistaken identity
(ii) Guilty but insane
(iii) Self-defence

109 (i) As a groom
(ii) As a manservant
(iii) As a gardener

110 (i) She was Polish
(ii) She was German
(iii) She was Dutch

111 (i) Her blind uncle
(ii) Her four-year-old
son
(iii) Her wheelchair-
bound husband

112 (i) USA
(ii) Switzerland
(iii) South Africa

113 (i) He pleaded insanity
(ii) He pleaded self-defence
(iii) He pleaded that there was no case to answer

114 (i) He was an art student
(ii) He was a postman
(iii) He was a chauffeur

115 (i) The robbery of the Bank of England
(ii) The assassination of the entire Cabinet
(iii) The robbery of a night mail train

116 (i) His huge hands
(ii) His bulging eyes
(iii) His tiny feet

117 (i) A clairvoyant
(ii) Television
(iii) Fax machines

118 (i) 'Flossie'
(ii) 'Ruby'
(iii) 'Phyllis'

119 (i) A public house
(ii) A hospital
(iii) A youth hostel

120 (i) She was a milliner's assistant
(ii) She was a waitress
(iii) She was a midwife's assistant

Question Rating (R5)

121 (i) A signet ring
(ii) A bowler hat
(iii) A tie

122 (i) A kitchen knife
(ii) A screwdriver
(iii) A dagger

123 (i) Cumbria
(ii) Cornwall
(iii) Cheshire

124 (i) He was a shipping clerk
(ii) He was a milliner
(iii) He was a bank clerk

125 (i) As a result of a road traffic accident
(ii) As a result of volunteering to be a Special Constable
(iii) As a result of being called to serve on a jury

126 (i) She had been a
pilot with the Polish
Air Force
   (ii) She had been a
secretary for
Winston Churchill
   (iii) She had been a
British Intelligence
Agent

127 (i) A flick knife
   (ii) A letter opener
   (iii) A clasp knife

128 (i) In a borstal
   (ii) In a mental home
   (iii) In a school

129 (i) Latin
   (ii) Esperanto
   (iii) Greek

130 (i) In a drinking club
   (ii) In a brothel
   (iii) In a striptease club

131 (i) He was a bus
conductor
   (ii) He was a laundry
van driver
   (iii) He was a publisher

132 (i) Wounding with
intent to murder the
same victim, his
wife
   (ii) Concealing the
discovery of
'Treasure Trove'
from a coroner
   (iii) Committing acts
preparatory to
treason

133 (i) Revenge – he
believed she had
libelled him in a
book
   (ii) Robbery – he was
out of work
   (iii) Jealousy – she was
in love with another
man

134 (i) A pair of scissors
   (ii) A letter opener
   (iii) A razor

135 (i) He was a journalist
   (ii) He was a soldier
   (iii) He was a banker

136 (i) Leeds
   (ii) Liverpool
   (iii) Manchester

137 (i) An engraved watch
   (ii) A monogrammed
handkerchief
   (iii) The key to the front
door of the victim's
house

138 (i) He was facing extradition to serve a prison sentence for a previous murder and she had begun divorce proceedings

(ii) He mistakenly believed his wife had been unfaithful and had infected him with syphilis

(iii) His wife was about to inform the police of his Mafia connections

139 (i) He was a cinema projectionist

(ii) He was a newspaper warehouseman

(iii) He was an art student

140 (i) A tradesman's van

(ii) A taxi cab

(iii) An army truck

141 (i) He was a welder

(ii) He was a scaffolder

(iii) He was a nightclub bouncer

142 (i) She was a circus fire-eater

(ii) She was a *Playboy* Bunny Girl

(iii) She was an Eastern belly-dancer

143 (i) In a supermarket

(ii) In a sauna

(iii) In a multi-storey car park

144 (i) Because she found that he had been involved in the death of her mother

(ii) Because he was a man with a history of violence against her and had tried to strangle her

(iii) Because he had encouraged their daughter to take up prostitution

145 (i) Hampshire

(ii) Norfolk

(iii) Essex

146 (i) An axe

(ii) A cleaver

(iii) A bread knife

147 (i) Greed – he robbed her of a few shillings

(ii) Fear – she was about to expose him as a bigamist

(iii) Jealousy – he thought his wife was having a love affair

148 (i) Norfolk
(ii) Suffolk
(iii) Kent

149 (i) He was a ship's
steward
(ii) He was a barman
(iii) He was a porter

150 (i) He was wanted for
murder
(ii) He suffered from the
same disfigurement
as the 'Elephant
Man'
(iii) He had deserted
from the forces in
the First World War

CHAPTER SIX

CLUES

Question Rating (R1)

1. (i) They had all been strangled
   (ii) They all had their throats cut
   (iii) They all had their necks broken

2. (i) 'The Beast of Marston Moor'
   (ii) 'The Yorkshire Ripper'
   (iii) 'Will o' The Wisp'

3. (i) 'The Red Devil'
   (ii) 'The Black Panther'
   (iii) 'The Grey Ghost'

4. (i) They were all vagrants
   (ii) They were all children's nannies
   (iii) They were all prostitutes

5. (i) Football
   (ii) Horse racing
   (iii) Boxing

6. (i) Lesley Whittle
   (ii) Susie Devaney
   (iii) Rita Gallagher

7. (i) He drugged them then cut their wrists
   (ii) He threw them overboard from a ship while on honeymoon
   (iii) He drowned them in a bath

8. (i) 'The Crematorium Killer'
   (ii) 'The Acid Bath Murderer'
   (iii) 'Quicklime Johnny'

9. (i) One
   (ii) Two
   (iii) Three

10 (i) Charles, Ronald and Raymond
   (ii) Ronald, Reginald and Charles
   (iii) Reginald, Charles and Eddie

11 (i) He was a cook
   (ii) He was unemployed
   (iii) He was a civil servant

12 (i) Two
   (ii) Three
   (iii) Four

13 (i) 'The Vampire Slayer'
   (ii) 'The Brides in the Bath Murderer'
   (iii) 'The Lambeth Poisoner'

14 (i) Never
   (ii) Once
   (iii) Twice

15 (i) 'The Elliot gang'
   (ii) 'The Richardson gang'
   (iii) 'The Carter Street Mob'

16 (i) Three
   (ii) Five
   (iii) Seven

17 (i) Edward Marshall Hall
   (ii) Sir Norman Birkett
   (iii) F. E. Smith

18 (i) She was killed in a room
   (ii) She was alive when found
   (iii) Her body was found in the River Thames

19 (i) His ability to escape and fade into obscurity after each of his crimes
   (ii) His fervent support of Manchester United Football Club
   (iii) The black hood which he wore when committing robberies

20 (i) Two
   (ii) Three
   (iii) Five

21 (i) Cumberland
   (ii) Cornwall
   (iii) Cheshire

22 (i) He had sexual intercourse with the corpses
   (ii) He drank fresh blood from the corpses
   (iii) He urinated over the corpses

23 (i) The Prince of Wales
   (ii) The Duke of York
   (iii) The Duke of Clarence

24 (i) They were students
   (ii) They were prostitutes
   (iii) They were nurses

25 (i) A West Country accent
   (ii) A Geordie accent
   (iii) A Scots accent

26 (i) Neither
   (ii) Reginald
   (iii) Ronald

27 (i) Most were strangled
   (ii) Most were stabbed to death
   (iii) Most were poisoned

28 (i) Holloway Prison
   (ii) Wandsworth Prison
   (iii) Wormwood Scrubs

29 (i) The eyes from a female victim
   (ii) The finger from a female victim
   (iii) Half a kidney from a female victim

30 (i) The Essex Constabulary
   (ii) The City of London Force
   (iii) The British Transport Police

Question Rating (R2)

31 (i) She was a prostitute
   (ii) She was a waitress
   (iii) She was a secretary

32 (i) Bristol
   (ii) Edinburgh
   (iii) London

33 (i) He was unusually tall (6′ 6″) and thin
   (ii) He had been born with a hump-back
   (iii) He was unusually short (5′ 4″) and bow-legged

34 (i) Rochester
   (ii) Canterbury
   (iii) Gravesend

35 (i) They were all sub-
postmasters

(ii) They were all
doctors

(iii) They were all
security guards

36 (i) They were all his
bigamous wives

(ii) They were all
prostitutes

(iii) They all had red hair

37 (i) William John Smith

(ii) Charles Frederick
Peace

(iii) Eric Godlewski

38 (i) Quicklime

(ii) Nitric acid

(iii) Sulphuric acid

39 (i) Two

(ii) Five

(iii) Seven

40 (i) He cut their throats

(ii) He strangled them

(iii) He broke their
necks

41 (i) They were both
army nurses

(ii) They were both
chorus girls

(iii) They were both
prostitutes

42 (i) 'Angelic Annie'

(ii) 'Dark Annie'

(iii) 'Anne Boleyn'

43 (i) A gun

(ii) An axe

(iii) A jemmy

44 (i) The Royal Navy

(ii) The Royal Air Force

(iii) The Army

45 (i) They were all
stabbed to death

(ii) They were all
repeatedly run over
by a car

(iii) They were all shot
dead

46 (i) Sylvia Sutcliffe

(ii) Sonia Sutcliffe

(iii) Shirley Sutcliffe

47 (i) Eire

(ii) USA

(iii) France

48 (i) He was stabbed in
the throat

(ii) He was shot in the
head

(iii) His skull was
smashed with an
axe

49 (i) In Wales

(ii) In Scotland

(iii) In the Channel
Islands

50
(i) Alfie Hines
(ii) Frank Mitchell
(iii) George Cooper

51
(i) Because he ran a hostel for young male vagrants
(ii) Because of an abnormally strong affection for his mother, he was incapable of hurting any female
(iii) Because he was a homosexual

52
(i) 'Jack the Lad'
(ii) 'Jack the Knife'
(iii) 'Jack the Hat'

53
(i) The Royal Air Force
(ii) The Army
(iii) The Royal Navy

54
(i) In an air raid shelter
(ii) On a bomb site
(iii) In an aircraft hangar

55
(i) He was a merchant seaman
(ii) He was a carpenter
(iii) He was a long-distance lorry driver

56
(i) Vera
(ii) Victoria
(iii) Violet

57
(i) A serially numbered ration book
(ii) A photograph of himself
(iii) A service issue gas mask

58
(i) He was stabbed to death with a carving knife
(ii) He was shot several times in the face
(iii) He was drowned in a bath

59
(i) 'The Mob'
(ii) 'The Firm'
(iii) 'The Family'

60
(i) Eton College
(ii) Rugby School
(iii) Harrow School

Question Rating (R3)

61
(i) An identical murder took place in the same location while Rowland was in custody

(ii) The chief prosecution witness, a one-time suspect, committed suicide

(iii) A man in custody for another offence confessed to the murder

62 (i) Superintendent Brian Forbes

(ii) Superintendent Robert Fabian

(iii) Superintendent Tommy Butler

63 (i) In a cave on a hillside

(ii) Under a wooden hut by an airfield

(iii) In a field near a farm

64 (i) In bed

(ii) In the bath

(iii) On the balcony

65 (i) London

(ii) Leeds

(iii) Manchester

66 (i) Jack the Ripper

(ii) Napoleon

(iii) Adolf Hitler

67 (i) Czechoslovakia

(ii) Sweden

(iii) Holland

68 (i) In the back garden

(ii) In a wood in North Wales

(iii) On Blackpool beach

69 (i) Derbyshire

(ii) Lancashire

(iii) Yorkshire

70 (i) He was a bus driver

(ii) He was a joiner

(iii) He was a miner

71 (i) Australia

(ii) South Africa

(iii) Canada

72 (i) He confessed to both murders

(ii) He was picked out on an identity parade which he requested

(iii) On both occasions he confided in his wife who informed on him

73 (i) Hull

(ii) Newcastle

(iii) Durham

74 (i) One
    (ii) Three
    (iii) Four

75 (i) He shot her in the neck
    (ii) He strangled her with piano wire
    (iii) He crushed her skull with a brick

76 (i) A disused aircraft hangar at the edge of a wood
    (ii) A tenement block stairwell, in Glasgow City Centre
    (iii) A lock-up garage in Pimlico, London

77 (i) The Royal Artillery
    (ii) The Royal Corps of Transport
    (iii) The Royal Fusiliers

78 (i) He shot them both with a revolver
    (ii) He poisoned them both with arsenic
    (iii) He strangled them both with his tie

79 (i) George Joseph Smith
    (ii) Dr Crippen
    (iii) Dr Neill Cream

80 (i) That he would adopt her children
    (ii) That he would see she was buried in her native Poland
    (iii) A suicide pact

81 (i) 'Killarney Liz'
    (ii) 'Strident Lizzie'
    (iii) 'Long Liz'

82 (i) Wales
    (ii) Scotland
    (iii) The Isle of Man

83 (i) He had beaten her to death with a hammer
    (ii) He had stabbed her to death with a carving knife
    (iii) He had strangled her with a piece of wire

84 (i) Edinburgh
    (ii) Dundee
    (iii) Glasgow

85 (i) He was a stockbroker
    (ii) He was a solicitor
    (iii) He was an antique dealer

86 (i) One
    (ii) Four
    (iii) Six

87 (i) Bethnal Green
(ii) Highgate
(iii) Greenwich

88 (i) He had been a nightwatchman
(ii) He had been a publican
(iii) He had been a policeman

89 (i) Cornwall
(ii) Yorkshire
(iii) Surrey

90 (i) He was a writer specializing in murder mystery stories
(ii) He was a butcher and public executioner
(iii) He was clerk to the Magistrates in the court where his son was charged with his murder

Question Rating (R4)

91 (i) 'The Man Who Knew Too Much'
(ii) 'The Man Who Smiled Too Much'
(iii) 'The Man Who Talked Too Much'

92 (i) A silver Jaguar 3.8
(ii) A white Mercedes limousine
(iii) A blue Standard Vanguard Estate

93 (i) They were all shot dead
(ii) They died as a result of an arson attack
(iii) They were all gassed to death

94 (i) Sussex
(ii) Derbyshire
(iii) Kent

95 (i) By means of its tattoos
(ii) Through a DNA comparison
(iii) The corpse had gallstones – and Moseley was known to suffer from them

96 (i) Harry Maurice Roberts
(ii) John Duddy
(iii) George Gray

97 (i) 'The Fort'
(ii) 'The Bunker'
(iii) 'The Castle'

98 (i) Six
(ii) Ten
(iii) Fifteen

99 (i) A poker
(ii) A rolling pin
(iii) A hammer

100 (i) His wife
(ii) His daughter
(iii) His brother

101 (i) Ten
(ii) Eleven
(iii) Thirteen

102 (i) Hampshire
(ii) Surrey
(iii) Lancashire

103 (i) Following a sexual
assault on a cell
mate
(ii) Following his face
being slashed with a
razor by a fellow
inmate
(iii) Following an
attempt at suicide
by slashing his
wrists

104 (i) A Jaguar
(ii) An Alvis
(iii) A Humber

105 (i) Right-wing, Fascist
affiliations
(ii) Strong left-wing
political sympathies
(iii) Scottish Nationalist
affiliations

106 (i) His wife informed
the police of her
suspicions
(ii) He was interviewed,
sitting in a car with a
prostitute, by vice-
squad officers
(iii) He was found hiding
in a garden with
housebreaking tools
in his possession

107 (i) Newcastle
(ii) Liverpool
(iii) Blackpool

108 (i) He was an
undertaker
(ii) He was a chauffeur
(iii) He was a fisherman

109 (i) By arsenic
poisoning
(ii) By a shotgun
(iii) With an axe

110 (i) A pair of coal tongs
(ii) A flat iron
(iii) A rolling pin

111 (i) He blasted them
with a shotgun
(ii) He stabbed them to
death
(iii) He bludgeoned
them to death with
the branch of a tree

112 (i) He was stopped in the street by police officers suspicious of his movements

(ii) He was informed on by his wife

(iii) He surrendered himself into police custody

113 (i) In the boot of a car

(ii) In a trunk in a loft

(iii) At the foot of some cliffs on a beach

114 (i) Greed – he was robbing Dyson who resisted

(ii) Jealousy – he wished to have an affair with Dyson's wife

(iii) Fear – he was on the run and Dyson recognized him

115 (i) One

(ii) Three

(iii) Six

116 (i) 'The King's Club'

(ii) 'The Big K's'

(iii) 'The Double R'

117 (i) He strangled them all

(ii) He stabbed them all

(iii) He poisoned them all

118 (i) 'Alpha Zulu Five'

(ii) 'Foxtrot One One'

(iii) 'India Nine Zero'

119 (i) They made use of military night-vision binoculars to observe the suspect after dark

(ii) They had cotton threads across gaps in the hedge which he broke when inspecting the graves at night

(iii) They painted the soles of his shoes with a compound which glowed in the presence of infra-red light

120 (i) Sir Charles Warren

(ii) Sir Melville MacNaghten

(iii) Sir Charles Rowan

Question Rating (R5)

121 (i) She committed suicide
     (ii) She died in childbirth
     (iii) She was killed in a road accident

122 (i) Donald Nolan
     (ii) Donald Nappey
     (iii) Donald Neumann

123 (i) The Household Cavalry
     (ii) The Northamptonshire Regiment
     (iii) The Royal Artillery

124 (i) The manufacture of imitation jewellery
     (ii) The manufacture of a new type of car battery
     (iii) The manufacture of artificial fingernails

125 (i) Betting shops
     (ii) Ice-cream vans
     (iii) Mini-cabs

126 (i) The Quakers
     (ii) The Plymouth Brethren
     (iii) The Jehovah's Witnesses

127 (i) Geoffrey Fox, Christopher Head and David Wombwell
     (ii) Sidney Miles, John Fairfax and George Gutteridge
     (iii) David Robertson, Timothy Wilson and Trevor Blackwell

128 (i) Three
     (ii) Six
     (iii) Nine

129 (i) In a car
     (ii) In a boat
     (iii) In a wheelbarrow

130 (i) Field and Gray
     (ii) Duddy and Witney
     (iii) Kassel and Browne

131 (i) A bread knife
     (ii) A tin opener
     (iii) A screwdriver

132 (i) In a public convenience
     (ii) On a bus
     (iii) In a swimming pool

133 (i) Poland
     (ii) Austria
     (iii) Germany

134 (i) Ten
     (ii) Twelve
     (iii) Fifteen

135 (i) Esmeralda's Barn
(ii) The Astor Club
(iii) The Uppercut Club

136 (i) Devon
(ii) Yorkshire
(iii) Hampshire

137 (i) He believed that she had infected him with venereal disease
(ii) He believed that she was going to the police because he was blackmailing her
(iii) He believed that she was going to have his baby

138 (i) He threw them both over a cliff
(ii) He shot them both in the head
(iii) He stabbed them both with a knife and hit the mother with an axe

139 (i) By strangulation
(ii) With a shotgun
(iii) By poisoning

140 (i) His wife
(ii) Peter Fell himself
(iii) His mother

141 (i) On cliffs overlooking the sea
(ii) In a wood
(iii) In a train compartment

142 (i) His wife and four children
(ii) His mother and father
(iii) His two brothers

143 (i) Poland
(ii) France
(iii) Czechoslovakia

144 (i) He was an insurance agent
(ii) He was a driving instructor
(iii) He was a train driver

145 (i) The Grenadier Guards
(ii) The Royal Corps of Transport
(iii) The Special Air Service

146 (i) Two
(ii) Four
(iii) Six

147 (i) He underwent cosmetic surgery to alter his appearance

(ii) He stowed away on a ship heading for South America

(iii) He left a note with his clothes, on a beach, suggesting he had committed suicide

148 (i) Nine

(ii) Sixteen

(iii) Twenty-one

149 (i) Because he had changed his story of the events no less than seven times before his trial

(ii) Because he had been convicted of manslaughter on a previous occasion and had told the same story

(iii) Because the blood found on the murder weapon was mostly his, indicating that his wound had been inflicted last

150 (i) He was a 'gigolo'

(ii) He was a soldier

(iii) He was a labourer

CHAPTER SEVEN

CLUES

Question Rating (R1)

1
(i) Ricky Hulton and Matilda Lewis
(ii) Raymond Fernandez and Martha Beck
(iii) Ian Brady and Myra Hindley

2
(i) She was a teacher
(ii) She was a childminder
(iii) She was a nurse

3
(i) Voice print comparison
(ii) Offender profiling
(iii) DNA fingerprinting

4
(i) They were all strangled
(ii) It has never been established
(iii) They were all bludgeoned to death

5
(i) She was a publican
(ii) She was a prostitute
(iii) She was a baby farmer

6
(i) He was a transvestite
(ii) He was a necrophiliac
(iii) He was a sado-masochist

7
(i) Newcastle
(ii) Norwich
(iii) Nottingham

8
(i) Buxton Moors
(ii) Saddleworth Moors
(iii) Ilkley Moors

9
(i) Sir Laurence Olivier
(ii) Sir Anthony Hopkins
(iii) Sir Richard Attenborough

10 (i)   Peter William
          Richardson
    (ii) Neville George
          Clevely Heath
    (iii) Edward Burrows

11 (i)   He shot her with a
          pistol
    (ii) He bludgeoned her
          to death with a car
          spanner
    (iii) He strangled her
          with a scarf

12 (i)   Lord Home
    (ii) Lord Longford
    (iii) Lord Lowery

13 (i)   Dartmoor Prison
    (ii) Rampton Hospital
    (iii) Broadmoor Hospital

14 (i)   London
    (ii) Manchester
    (iii) Glasgow

15 (i)   Nobody
    (ii) Ian David Hay
    (iii) Frederick Abeline

16 (i)   Irish
    (ii) Canadian
    (iii) British

17 (i)   Sidney Fox
    (ii) Winston Goode
    (iii) Maxwell Confait

18 (i)   Edinburgh
    (ii) London
    (iii) Cardiff

19 (i)   Samples of female
          pubic hair
    (ii) Severed female
          nipples
    (iii) Severed finger tips

20 (i)   A road haulage firm
    (ii) A chemicals firm
    (iii) A tool
          manufacturing firm

21 (i)   By using hypnosis
    (ii) By using sleeping
          pills
    (iii) By using coal gas

22 (i)   A fire engine driver
    (ii) An ARP warden
    (iii) A War Reserve
          policeman

23 (i)   Ten years old
    (ii) Eleven years old
    (iii) Fifteen years old

24 (i)   Scotland
    (ii) The Isle of Wight
    (iii) Wales

25 (i)   Wigan, Lancashire
    (ii) Halifax, Yorkshire
    (iii) Keswick, Cumbria

26 (i)   Manchester
    (ii) Leeds
    (iii) Liverpool

27 (i) 'The Stockwell
Strangler'
(ii) 'The Streatham
Slayer'
(iii) 'The Deptford Devil'

28 (i) Cognitive
interviewing of
witnesses
(ii) DNA fingerprinting
(iii) Psychological
offender profiling

29 (i) Vagrants
(ii) Male homosexuals
(iii) Prostitutes

30 (i) He was painting the
windows of his
aunt's house
(ii) He was on his
newspaper round
(iii) He was making
deliveries for a local
baker

Question Rating (R2)

31 (i) South Africa
(ii) Australia
(iii) Canada

32 (i) He was strangled
(ii) His throat was cut
(iii) He was poisoned

33 (i) Communist
(ii) Nazi
(iii) Republican

34 (i) The 'Railway Killer'
(ii) The 'Towpath
Murderer'
(iii) The 'Airport
Assassin'

35 (i) He was shot in the
head
(ii) He was strangled
(iii) He was kicked to
death

36 (i) 'The Madman'
(ii) 'The Gorilla Man'
(iii) 'The Wolf Man'

37 (i) He was a
blacksmith
(ii) He was a chauffeur
(iii) He was a sailor

38 (i) In a disused coal
mine
(ii) In a cave near a
beach
(iii) In a forest

39 (i) He was thrown from
a second-floor
bedroom window
(ii) He was drowned in
a bath
(iii) He was bludgeoned
to death with an axe

40 (i) 'Do you have a
malt, old boy?'
(ii) 'I'll just finish this,
then we can be on
our way'
(iii) 'In the
circumstances, you
might make that a
double!'

41 (i) A dumb-bell
(ii) An axe
(iii) A belt

42 (i) The Royal Air Force
(ii) The Royal Navy
(iii) The Army

43 (i) Sixty-two years old
(ii) Fifteen years old
(iii) Twelve years old

44 (i) They were stabbed
to death
(ii) They were drowned
(iii) They were shot in
the head

45 (i) Walsall,
Staffordshire
(ii) Halifax, Yorkshire
(iii) Paddington, London

46 (i) A railway porter
(ii) A passing police
officer
(iii) Two women who
were opening a
children's home

47 (i) She had been
strangled
(ii) She had been
poisoned
(iii) She had been
neglected and
starved to death

48 (i) He was a taxi driver
(ii) He was a
bookmaker
(iii) He was a church
caretaker

49 (i) He was bludgeoned
(ii) He was strangled
(iii) He was poisoned

50 (i) A pair of
knuckledusters
(ii) A bicycle chain
(iii) A leather riding whip

51 (i) Mentally retarded
children
(ii) Elderly men and
women
(iii) Male homosexuals

52 (i) Accidental death
(ii) Attack by a wild
animal
(iii) Attempted rape

53 (i) Spain
(ii) Czechoslovakia
(iii) Italy

54 (i) He was her uncle
(ii) He was her stepfather
(iii) He was her brother

55 (i) 'The Carbon Copy Murders'
(ii) 'The Copycat Murders'
(iii) 'The Hitchhiker Murders'

56 (i) They were both solicitors
(ii) They were both teachers
(iii) They were both missionaries

57 (i) They were grave robbers
(ii) They were cooks who used human flesh in their pies
(iii) They disposed of other women's unwanted babies

58 (i) Two
(ii) Four
(iii) None

59 (i) Her neck was broken with a karate blow
(ii) She was thrown alive from a moving car

(iii) Her head was smashed against a wall

60 (i) Three
(ii) Four
(iii) Six

Question Rating (R3)

61 (i) The Army
(ii) The Royal Air Force
(iii) The Royal Army Service Corps

62 (i) The weapon was taken home, for his own use, by a policeman who found it in a police car
(ii) They disposed of it as lost property at an auction before the trial
(iii) It was returned, in error, to the accused man before his trial

63 (i) Devon
(ii) Suffolk
(iii) Cumbria

64 (i) Two
(ii) Four
(iii) More than he could remember

65 (i) Suffolk
(ii) Kent
(iii) Buckinghamshire

66 (i) A women's lavatory at a railway station
(ii) The steps of the National Portrait Gallery
(iii) In the Serpentine at Hyde Park

67 (i) They were all poisoned
(ii) They were all strangled
(iii) They were all bludgeoned to death with his fists

68 (i) Lancashire
(ii) Leicestershire
(iii) Huntingdonshire

69 (i) She strangled him
(ii) She blasted him with a shotgun
(iii) She cut his throat with a razor

70 (i) Four
(ii) Six
(iii) Seven

71 (i) He bludgeoned her to death
(ii) He stabbed her to death
(iii) He drowned her

72 (i) Three
(ii) Four
(iii) Seven

73 (i) Greed – he robbed her of her jewellery
(ii) Lust – she died during the course of a rape
(iii) Fear – he believed she would give evidence against him for sexually abusing her

74 (i) She was his half-sister
(ii) She was his aunt
(iii) She was his mother

75 (i) Three
(ii) Four
(iii) Five

76 (i) They were both blind
(ii) They were both homosexuals
(iii) They were both bookmakers

77 (i) They were all written in red ink
(ii) They all contained significant spelling errors
(iii) They were all in different handwriting

78 (i) A shotgun
(ii) Chocolates laced with arsenic
(iii) An axe

79 (i) They obtained the photographs of every male in the vicinity of the scene of crime at the relevant time and showed them to their only witness, who was too infirm to attend an identification parade
(ii) They fingerprinted every male over the age of sixteen believed possibly to have been in the vicinity of the scene of crime at the relevant time
(iii) They interviewed, on cine-film, every convicted and suspected child molester in Great Britain

80 (i) Warwickshire
(ii) Surrey
(iii) Devon

81 (i) Lesley Ann Downey
(ii) Pauline Reade
(iii) Ann Kilbride

82 (i) He was an ice-cream salesman
(ii) He was a schoolteacher
(iii) He was a lorry driver

83 (i) She was a typist
(ii) She was an accounts clerk
(iii) She was a canteen manageress

84 (i) A pilot
(ii) A doctor
(iii) A butcher

85 (i) He was a warehouseman
(ii) He was a stock clerk
(iii) He was a driver

86 (i) She believed she was possessed by an evil voodoo spirit
(ii) She believed the children were dying of AIDS
(iii) She believed the children were conspiring to kill her

87 (i) 'Cut-em-up-Christie'
 (ii) 'Reggie-no-dick'
 (iii) 'The Corpse'

88 (i) Devon
 (ii) Hampshire
 (iii) Derbyshire

89 (i) He used a ladder
 placed on a fire
 escape and entered
 his room through a
 window
 (ii) He sounded the fire
 alarm; then, with the
 evacuated guests
 on the lawn, he
 entered his room
 (iii) He fused all the
 hotel lights from an
 outside junction box,
 then entered his
 room in the ensuing
 confusion

90 (i) On a routine
 inspection of Heys'
 billet, he discovered
 the murder weapon
 (ii) He received an
 anonymous letter,
 which was proved to
 have been written
 by Heys, containing
 incriminating
 evidence

 (iii) Heys' wife told his
 commanding officer
 that the alibi
 evidence she was
 about to give was
 false

Question Rating (R4)

91 (i) Squadron Leader
 Robert Browning
 (ii) Group Captain
 Rupert Brooke
 (iii) Lieutenant Wilfred
 Owen

92 (i) He claimed to have
 killed the child while
 trying to resuscitate
 him after he had
 stopped breathing
 (ii) He claimed to have
 killed the child by
 administering
 poison in the dark
 from a bottle whose
 shape was the
 same as one for
 medicine
 (iii) He claimed to have
 killed while suffering
 a nightmare in his
 sleep

93 (i) She had her skull smashed with a tyre lever
(ii) She was stabbed to death with a bayonet
(iii) She was suffocated

94 (i) The Welsh Guards
(ii) The Royal Army Medical Corps
(iii) The Parachute Regiment

95 (i) He was a school caretaker
(ii) He was a park keeper
(iii) He was a builder's labourer

96 (i) The murders of two other children
(ii) The 'Cannock Chase' murders
(iii) The murder of a fellow prisoner

97 (i) Tunbridge Wells, Kent
(ii) Guildford, Surrey
(iii) Bournemouth, Dorset

98 (i) Approximately six months
(ii) Approximately two years

(iii) Approximately ten years

99 (i) Norma Joyce Bell
(ii) Elizabeth Watson
(iii) June Brown

100 (i) A shoe shop
(ii) A seed merchant
(iii) A fish and chip shop

101 (i) The Royal Artillery
(ii) The Scots Guards
(iii) The Royal Corps of Signals

102 (i) In a cinema where he worked as a projectionist
(ii) In Brixton Prison
(iii) In France during the First World War

103 (i) He had been bludgeoned to death
(ii) He had been suffocated
(iii) He had been stabbed to death

104 (i) He worked in a timber mill
(ii) He worked in a brickworks
(iii) He worked in a flour mill

105 (i) Rampton Hospital
(ii) Broadmoor Hospital
(iii) Cookham Wood Prison

106 (i) Brick dust
(ii) Car engine oil
(iii) Dog hairs

107 (i) He was delivering a newspaper on his round
(ii) He was breaking into the house
(iii) He was doing household chores as part of his Boy Scout 'Bob-a-Job' week

108 (i) She was a children's governess
(ii) She was a ballet dancer
(iii) She was an authoress

109 (i) He pleaded that his wife had attacked him and he had acted in self-defence
(ii) He pleaded that there had been a suicide pact with his wife
(iii) He pleaded the mercy killing of his terminally ill wife

110 (i) Joseph Brown
(ii) David Smith
(iii) Ronald Jones

111 (i) A hammer
(ii) A candlestick
(iii) A lead weight for a sash window

112 (i) Cornwall
(ii) Cheshire
(iii) Yorkshire

113 (i) Necrophilic characteristics
(ii) Sado-homosexual characteristics
(iii) Paedophilic characteristics

114 (i) Her neck was broken
(ii) She was drowned in a bath
(iii) She was strangled with her own tights

115 (i) Wiltshire
(ii) Surrey
(iii) Sussex

116 (i) She was shot with a pistol
(ii) She was stabbed to death
(iii) She was suffocated

117 (i) Essex
(ii) Hampshire
(iii) Middlesex

118 (i) He poisoned them
(ii) He stabbed them to death
(iii) He strangled them

119 (i) Yorkshire
(ii) Herefordshire
(iii) Surrey

120 (i) He was a student
(ii) He was a soldier
(iii) He was a milkman

Question Rating (R5)

121 (i) Worcestershire
(ii) Cumbria
(iii) Cornwall

122 (i) In a public house
(ii) In a workhouse
(iii) In a public swimming baths

123 (i) He had been an assistant chef
(ii) He had been an apprentice printer
(iii) He had been a post office manager

124 (i) In a coal cellar
(ii) In a garden air-raid shelter

(iii) In a divan base in the home

125 (i) She was twelve years old
(ii) She was sixteen years old
(iii) She was ten years old

126 (i) She was a writer
(ii) She was a cook
(iii) She was a midwife

127 (i) She strangled her with a garden clothes line
(ii) She smashed her head against a wall
(iii) She drowned her in a cesspool

128 (i) Her sister's child
(ii) Her own child
(iii) Her brother's child

129 (i) He was a packer in a flour mill
(ii) He was a hospital porter
(iii) He was a security guard

130 (i) Four
(ii) Six
(iii) Nine

131 (i) Lesley Ann Downey
(ii) Pauline Reade
(iii) Keith Bennett

132 (i) He was eight months old
(ii) He was two years old
(iii) He was four years old

133 (i) The Army
(ii) The Royal Air Force
(iii) The Royal Navy

134 (i) Benjamin Disraeli
(ii) The Duke of Kent
(iii) The Prince of Wales

135 (i) He garrotted them
(ii) He pushed a screwdriver into their ears
(iii) He suffocated them by placing a plastic bag over their heads

136 (i) He was an architect
(ii) He was a stockbroker
(iii) He was a deputy inspector of factories

137 (i) Three
(ii) Five
(iii) Seven

138 (i) A Renault Dauphine
(ii) A bubble car
(iii) A motor cycle and sidecar

139 (i) Irrefutable forensic evidence
(ii) 'Evidence of System' (i.e. previous poisonings)
(iii) Documentary evidence showing how she planned the murder

140 (i) Bath
(ii) Edinburgh
(iii) London

141 (i) Two
(ii) Three
(iii) Five

142 (i) An atlas of the world
(ii) A diary
(iii) A prayer book

143 (i) He was a building site labourer
(ii) He was a milkman
(iii) He was a sailor

144 (i) He was French
(ii) He was English
(iii) He was American

145 (i) Alzheimer's Disease
(ii) Munchausen Syndrome
(iii) Locks Syndrome

146 (i) Southend-on-Sea, Essex
(ii) Brighton, Sussex
(iii) Bournemouth, Dorset

147 (i) John Reginald Halliday Christie
(ii) Gordon Frederick Cummins
(iii) Neville George Clevely Heath

148 (i) A walking stick
(ii) A bottle top
(iii) A coin

149 (i) Richard Attenborough
(ii) Jack Hawkins
(iii) George Sanders

150 (i) He pushed her head into a fish bowl where he held it until she drowned
(ii) He tied her hand to a light socket and electrocuted her
(iii) He suffocated her by wrapping clingfilm around her face

CHAPTER EIGHT

CLUES

Question Rating (R1)

1   (i)   Dennis Nilsen
    (ii) John Reginald
          Halliday Christie
    (iii) Neville Heath

2   (i)   Deptford
    (ii) Bermondsey
    (iii) Whitechapel

3   (i)   At the front door of
          his London flat
    (ii) On the ramp of the
          House of Commons
          underground car
          park
    (iii) In the New Forest,
          Hampshire

4   (i)   'The London
          Hospital Tavern'
    (ii) 'The Blind Beggar'
    (iii) 'The White Horse'

5   (i)   Glasgow
    (ii) Dundee
    (iii) Edinburgh

6   (i)   A cinema
    (ii) A public house
    (iii) A hotel

7   (i)   Under the cellar
          floor
    (ii) In the attic
    (iii) In the back garden

8   (i)   'The Ratcliffe
          Highway Murders'
    (ii) 'The Seven Dials
          Murders'
    (iii) 'The Cato Street
          Murders'

9   (i)   In the House of
          Lords, Westminster
    (ii) In the House of
          Commons,
          Westminster
    (iii) In the Guildhall, City
          of London

10 (i)   Mrs Mary McCann
    (ii) Mrs Muriel McKay
    (iii) Mrs Margaret
          Murdoch

11 (i) In a police station
(ii) On the roof of a warehouse
(iii) At a railway station

12 (i) It flooded when the water mains burst
(ii) It burned to the ground
(iii) It was blown apart by a military cannon

13 (i) 39 Hilldrop Crescent, W7
(ii) 25 Menlove Gardens East, E3
(iii) 10 Rillington Place, W11

14 (i) London
(ii) Cardiff
(iii) Glasgow

15 (i) In a seaside hotel
(ii) On the beach
(iii) In a fishing boat

16 (i) Hypostasis
(ii) Post-mortem lividity
(iii) Rigor mortis

17 (i) The Metropole Hotel
(ii) The Royal Hotel
(iii) The Grand Hotel

18 (i) Hanging from the north arch of Blackfriars Bridge
(ii) Floating, face down, in the River Thames
(iii) Lying, near an empty bottle of sleeping pills, in Hyde Park

19 (i) He blew himself and his victim to death with a parcel bomb
(ii) He shot him in the head with a revolver
(iii) He stabbed him in the neck with a knife

20 (i) By a palm print
(ii) By handwriting comparison
(iii) By a voice print comparison

21 (i) Iraq's
(ii) Iran's
(iii) Libya's

22 (i) William Ewart Gladstone's
(ii) Benjamin Disraeli's
(iii) Sir Robert Peel's

23 (i) The tea rooms at the Crystal Palace
(ii) Lyons Corner House
(iii) The restaurant at the Windmill Theatre

24 (i) 'The Murder Bag'
(ii) 'The Bone Bag'
(iii) 'The Watson Bag'

25 (i) On a sandy beach
(ii) On a mountainside
(iii) In a peat bog

26 (i) Dismembered in some pig feed
(ii) It was never found
(iii) In a trunk at a Polish railway station

27 (i) Striation marks
(ii) Muzzle dirt
(iii) Powder burns

28 (i) Hampshire
(ii) Lincolnshire
(iii) Essex

29 (i) Buckingham Palace Road
(ii) Waterloo Bridge
(iii) Fleet Street

30 (i) Essex
(ii) Hampshire
(iii) Devon

Question Rating (R2)

31 (i) They both mysteriously burned down later in the year
(ii) They were both believed to be haunted by ghosts
(iii) They were the same building, Lancaster Castle

32 (i) A country house
(ii) A museum
(iii) A hospital

33 (i) A boomerang
(ii) An anti-tank mine
(iii) A black mamba snake

34 (i) In a schoolhouse
(ii) In a car
(iii) In a theatre

35 (i) In a wood
(ii) In a disused mine shaft
(iii) In a sewage tunnel

36 (i) The Richardson brothers
(ii) The Kray brothers
(iii) The Hosein brothers

37 (i) In a shop
(ii) At his office
(iii) On a train

38 (i) Peter Sutcliffe
(ii) Dennis Nilsen
(iii) Kenneth Halliwell

39 (i) The Lake District
(ii) Scotland
(iii) Wales

40 (i) That every object at the centre of a scene of crime will, to varying degrees, bear traces of the perpetrator
(ii) That for every action there is an equal and opposite reaction
(iii) That when two objects come into contact, material from each will leave a trace on the other

41 (i) In the River Thames
(ii) In the walls of his house
(iii) In a trunk in a furniture depository

42 (i) Footprints
(ii) Tyre marks
(iii) Cigarette butts

43 (i) A haberdasher's shop and a public house
(ii) A candle maker's shop and a jeweller's
(iii) A ship's chandlers and a pawnbroker's shop

44 (i) The *Titanic*
(ii) The *Mauretania*
(iii) The *Lusitania*

45 (i) The office of the Chief Constable of the police area
(ii) A high court judge
(iii) The office of the Home Secretary

46 (i) Northumbria
(ii) Cumbria
(iii) Yorkshire

47 (i) Adipocere
(ii) Hypostasis
(iii) Secretion

48 (i) In a lunatic asylum
(ii) In a prisoner-of-war camp
(iii) In a submarine

49 (i) With a rifle
(ii) With an axe
(iii) With arsenic poisoning

50 (i) India
(ii) Germany
(iii) Ireland

51 (i) Human hair
(ii) Human nail fragments
(iii) Human teeth

52 (i) A shotgun
(ii) Poisoned food
(iii) A sword

53 (i) Whitechapel
(ii) Hampstead
(iii) Lambeth

54 (i) A police station
(ii) A theatre
(iii) A railway station

55 (i) The Ritz Hotel
(ii) The Savoy Hotel
(iii) The Dorchester Hotel

56 (i) Hanging by the neck from a beam in a hut
(ii) In the ground under a chicken run
(iii) In a sack of pig feed

57 (i) Croydon, Surrey
(ii) Epping, Essex
(iii) Barnet, Hertfordshire

58 (i) Kew Gardens
(ii) The Royal Observatory
(iii) In the River Thames

59 (i) A spent bullet
(ii) A crossbow bolt
(iii) A boomerang

60 (i) Limehouse
(ii) Soho
(iii) Notting Hill

Question Rating (R3)

61 (i) Southend-on-Sea, Essex
(ii) Brighton, Sussex
(iii) Margate, Kent

62 (i) Fragments of her fingers
(ii) Her plastic dentures
(iii) Fragments of hair

63 (i) Some sacks of pot-pourri
(ii) Several packets of mothballs
(iii) Two open tins of paint

64 (i) London
(ii) Leeds
(iii) Liverpool

65 (i) A wheelbarrow
(ii) A pram
(iii) An invalid chair

66 (i) In a ditch
(ii) In a taxi cab
(iii) In a shop

67 (i) In a crematorium
(ii) On a pig farm
(iii) On an ocean liner

68 (i) Locked in the boot of his car
(ii) Locked in a milk depot cold store
(iii) Locked in his attic

69 (i) In a wood
(ii) In a cemetery
(iii) In a church

70 (i) Naval cutlasses
(ii) Duelling swords
(iii) Duelling pistols

71 (i) A lunatic asylum
(ii) A prison
(iii) An army camp

72 (i) On a school cricket field
(ii) On a golf course
(iii) In a soccer stadium

73 (i) Leeds
(ii) Manchester
(iii) Liverpool

74 (i) Swords
(ii) Axes
(iii) Guns

75 (i) He was shot by a police marksman while apparently giving himself up
(ii) He shot himself with his own gun

(iii) He shot his hostage then took his own life with poison

76 (i) 'T-R-A-C-E-Y'
(ii) 'T-E-C'
(iii) 'H-O-L-M-E-S'

77 (i) She boiled her alive
(ii) She ill-treated and starved her to death
(iii) She slashed her throat with a knife

78 (i) He was an author
(ii) He was an actor
(iii) He was a policeman

79 (i) A post box
(ii) The front seat of a car
(iii) The carrier of a bicycle

80 (i) In a dustbin
(ii) In a trunk
(iii) In a sack

81 (i) A gypsy encampment
(ii) A fairground boxing booth
(iii) The cellar of a striptease club

82 (i) Tachbrook Street
(ii) Braybrook Street
(iii) Bessborough Street

83 (i) Flour
(ii) Car spray paint
(iii) Brewer's yeast

84 (i) King's Cross
(ii) Waterloo
(iii) Victoria

85 (i) Bethnal Green
(ii) Hackney
(iii) Stoke Newington

86 (i) In a drainage ditch
(ii) Under the floor of a barn
(iii) In a hay-loft

87 (i) In a trunk in the hall
(ii) In the attic in a sack
(iii) In the garden shed

88 (i) On waste ground
(ii) In the boot of a car
(iii) In a trunk in a left luggage office

89 (i) Marston Moor
(ii) Cannock Chase
(iii) Deadman's Hill

90 (i) In their own dining room
(ii) At a synagogue
(iii) In a nursing home

Question Rating (R4)

91 (i) In Hong Kong
(ii) In Cyprus
(iii) In Germany

92 (i) In a shop
(ii) In a cinema
(iii) In a hotel

93 (i) A tent peg
(ii) A Saxon sword
(iii) A hay fork

94 (i) In a van
(ii) In a basement flat
(iii) In a drain

95 (i) The height and weight ratio from footprints
(ii) The pattern of teeth formation from bite marks
(iii) The skin colour and racial type from hair samples

96 (i) He stunned the victim with a blow to the head, put his head into an oven and turned on the gas

    (ii) He stunned the victim with a blow to the head then hanged him with a pyjama cord

    (iii) He stunned the victim with a blow to the head then cut his wrists

97 (i) In a hotel

    (ii) In a theatre

    (iii) In a television studio

98 (i) Claridges Hotel

    (ii) The Savoy Hotel

    (iii) The Hilton Hotel

99 (i) In a horse trough

    (ii) In a fenland dyke

    (iii) In The Wash

100 (i) It was burnt in an engine room furnace

    (ii) It was pushed through the porthole of a ship into the ocean

    (iii) It was dissolved in acid

101 (i) In a dustbin

    (ii) In a car

    (iii) In a telephone kiosk

102 (i) In a pawnbroker's shop

    (ii) In a tailor's shop

    (iii) In a jeweller's shop

103 (i) German

    (ii) French

    (iii) Dutch

104 (i) He was face down in a puddle

    (ii) He was crucified on a wooden plank

    (iii) He was tied up and gagged

105 (i) Forest Gate

    (ii) Clapham

    (iii) Hendon

106 (i) A YWCA hostel

    (ii) A mill

    (iii) A school

107 (i) Sherwood Forest

    (ii) The New Forest

    (iii) Epping Forest

108 (i) On a train

    (ii) On a boat

    (iii) In a police van

109 (i) Liverpool

    (ii) Southampton

    (iii) Plymouth

110 (i) Bristol, Avon and Somerset
(ii) Southampton, Hampshire
(iii) Bradford, Yorkshire

111 (i) A cinema
(ii) A fairground
(iii) A gravel pit

112 (i) A cigarette butt
(ii) A piece of bandage made of materials used in military dressings
(iii) A naval cap badge

113 (i) Edinburgh
(ii) Liverpool
(iii) London

114 (i) Poole, Dorset
(ii) Brighton, Sussex
(iii) Margate, Kent

115 (i) A pool in the country
(ii) The top of a mountain
(iii) A beach

116 (i) In a school yard
(ii) In a cemetery
(iii) In a fairground

117 (i) At a cavalry barracks
(ii) On a ship on the high seas
(iii) In a public house

118 (i) A courthouse
(ii) A police station
(iii) A prison

119 (i) Floating in a river
(ii) Lying on a rubbish dump
(iii) Hanging in a drainage ditch

120 (i) Over ten years
(ii) Over twenty years
(iii) Over thirty years

Question Rating (R5)

121 (i) In a disused mineshaft
(ii) In a Peak District cave
(iii) In a lake

122 (i) In his taxi cab
(ii) In his bath
(iii) In the local cinema

123 (i) Manchester
(ii) York
(iii) Leeds

124 (i) A bootlace and a cufflink
(ii) A watch and a signet ring
(iii) A badge and a button

125 (i) Sir Winston
Churchill
(ii) General Eisenhower
(iii) The King of Greece

126 (i) Corsetry
(ii) A vacuum cleaner
(iii) Furniture

127 (i) Military manoeuvres
(ii) A hunt for an army
deserter
(iii) A game-shooting
trip

128 (i) In an unoccupied
summer house
(ii) In an unoccupied
church
(iii) In an unoccupied
stable block

129 (i) Because it had his
fingerprints on it
(ii) Because it was of a
special type only
issued to members
of the armed forces
(iii) Because it
destroyed the
prisoner's alibi for
the time of the
murder

130 (i) In a quarry
(ii) In a trunk washed
up on a beach

(iii) In the walls of his
house

131 (i) A raincoat and a
plastic bag
(ii) A gun and a leather
glove
(iii) Sunglasses and a
handkerchief

132 (i) At his newspaper's
offices
(ii) In a Soho nightclub
(iii) In his basement flat

133 (i) The Three Pawnbroker's Balls
(ii) The Sun, Moon and
Stars
(iii) The Three Wise
Monkeys

134 (i) In the privy
(ii) In the billiard room
(iii) In the summer
house

135 (i) He was digging
ditches
(ii) He was thatching
the farmhouse roof
(iii) He was poaching
rabbits

136 (i) In a nursing home
(ii) In a hospital
(iii) In her corner shop

137 (i) It is the highest village in England

(ii) It is the site of the last public hanging of a witch in England

(iii) It is sumberged under a reservoir

138 (i) A love letter and a naval uniform button

(ii) His revolver and a pair of gloves

(iii) A monogrammed handkerchief and a tie pin

139 (i) An air-raid shelter

(ii) A concrete pillbox

(iii) An aircraft hangar

140 (i) Englefield Green

(ii) Chobham

(iii) Guildford

141 (i) Wasps

(ii) Maggots of the bluebottle fly

(iii) Butterfly larvae

142 (i) A fishmonger's shop

(ii) A haberdasher's shop

(iii) A sweet shop

143 (i) A finger stall

(ii) A bandage

(iii) An eye patch

144 (i) The Isle of Wight

(ii) Hayling Island

(iii) The Isle of Dogs

145 (i) The cellar of a public house

(ii) A brothel

(iii) An empty blitzed shop

146 (i) In a sanatorium

(ii) In a prison

(iii) In a brothel

147 (i) A cinema

(ii) A nightclub

(iii) A hotel

148 (i) A block of flats

(ii) A school

(iii) A court house

149 (i) She was the first murderer in Britain known to have used strychnine as a poison and the last to be beheaded

(ii) She was the first murderess to be 'drawn and quartered' and the last to have attempted to claim 'Benefit of Clergy' as a defence

(iii) She was the first murderer caught as a result of distributing parts of her victim around London and the last to be burned at the stake for petty treason (i.e. murdering a husband)

150 (i) A bus garage

(ii) A cinema

(iii) A pie and mash shop

CHAPTER NINE

CLUES

Question Rating (R1)

1.
   (i) It is believed to have been dropped into the sea from a light aircraft
   (ii) It is believed that it was fed to pigs on a farm
   (iii) It is believed to have been concreted into a motorway

2.
   (i) It was the first time a murder conviction based on fingerprint evidence had been returned in a British court
   (ii) It was the first time that evidence of hair samples had been admitted in a murder trial
   (iii) It was the first time that a defendant in a murder trial had been allowed to give evidence in his own defence in a British court

3.
   (i) Cindy
   (ii) Kitten
   (iii) Bambi

4.
   (i) He was shot dead
   (ii) He was kidnapped then beaten to death
   (iii) He was blown to pieces in his car by a bomb

5   (i) Whether his
        behaviour gives rise
        to a plea of self-
        defence
   (ii) Whether his
        behaviour is sane
   (iii) Whether his
        behaviour amounts
        to causing grievous
        bodily harm

6   (i) He was Irish
   (ii) He was American
   (iii) He was South
        African

7   (i) Montreal, Canada
   (ii) Paris, France
   (iii) Berlin, Germany

8   (i) Rudyard Kipling
   (ii) Oscar Wilde
   (iii) George Bernard
        Shaw

9   (i) That she was a
        reincarnation of
        Joan of Arc
   (ii) That she was
        pregnant
   (iii) That she was really
        a man

10 (i) A doctor in the court
   (ii) A coroner's jury
   (iii) A shorthand writer
        to keep records

11 (i) It was the first time,
        in English Criminal
        Law, that anyone
        had been convicted
        of murder without
        the victim's body
        being found
   (ii) It was the first
        murder trial in
        Wales which
        permitted female
        jurors to be
        empanelled
   (iii) It was the last time a
        Welsh court passed
        sentence of death
        on a defendant

12 (i) By strangulation
   (ii) In a series of arson
        attacks
   (iii) By poisoning the
        domestic water
        supply

13 (i) Three
   (ii) Five
   (iii) Seven

14 (i) Provocation
   (ii) Insanity
   (iii) Self-defence

15 (i) By the tolling of a bell
    (ii) By the firing of a cannon
    (iii) By the raising of a black flag

16 (i) Seventeen years of age
    (ii) Twelve years of age
    (iii) Ten years of age

17 (i) From using sheep dip solution
    (ii) From spreading weed-killing solution
    (iii) From a tin of rat poison stored near food in the larder

18 (i) They were British
    (ii) They were Irish
    (iii) They were Americans

19 (i) Calcroft
    (ii) Pierrepoint
    (iii) Marwood

20 (i) As the rope was placed round his neck a last minute notice of stay of execution arrived and he was reprieved

(ii) He died of a heart attack before he could be hanged
(iii) After three unsuccessful attempts to hang him, he was reprieved

21 (i) Dr Hawley Harvey Crippen
    (ii) George Joseph Smith
    (iii) Frederick Seddon

22 (i) Suicide
    (ii) An open verdict
    (iii) Murder by person or persons unknown

23 (i) Florida, USA
    (ii) Broadmoor Hospital
    (iii) Dartmoor Prison

24 (i) The Parachute Regiment
    (ii) The Royal Army Medical Corps
    (iii) The Welsh Guards

25 (i) That he was suffering from amnesia
    (ii) That he was under the influence of a voodoo spell
    (iii) That his twin brother was the murderer

26 (i)   Malaya
(ii) Cyprus
(iii) West Germany

27 (i)   Duke Street Prison
(ii) Barlinnie Prison
(iii) Saughton Prison

28 (i)   Six months
(ii) A year and a day
(iii) Seven years

29 (i)   The Commissioner's Crime Collection
(ii) The Museum of London
(iii) The Black Museum

30 (i)   Interpol
(ii) Special Branch
(iii) The Extradition Squad

Question Rating (R2)

31 (i)   Not proven
(ii) Guilty of murder
(iii) Guilty but insane

32 (i)   He became a religious convert
(ii) He confessed to the murder
(iii) He made a will

33 (i)   It was never established
(ii) His brother
(iii) His mother

34 (i)   He was killed in the Russian Civil War
(ii) He starved himself to death in prison
(iii) He died in a duel in France

35 (i)   A prison
(ii) A lunatic asylum
(iii) A military hospital

36 (i)   The trial judge inadvertently referred to the defendant's criminal record in his summing up
(ii) Jurors were bribed to return a not-guilty verdict
(iii) A guilty man was found innocent

37 (i)   Brixton Prison
(ii) Wandsworth Prison
(iii) Wormwood Scrubs Prison

38 (i) The trial judge had misdirected the jury on the acceptability of a 'corroborated' statement by a witness

(ii) A key prosecution witness subsequently admitted, in a dying declaration, that he had lied at the trial

(iii) The defendant had been convicted mainly on hearsay evidence, which had not been challenged

39 (i) Both were found guilty

(ii) He was found guilty and she not guilty

(iii) She was found guilty and he not guilty

40 (i) 'Culpable homicide'

(ii) 'Unlawful killing'

(iii) 'Suspected homicide'

41 (i) Evidence of similar crimes committed by the defendant

(ii) Evidence of all the defendant's previous convictions

(iii) Evidence from previous similar trials showing the juries' decisions in those cases

42 (i) The Homicide Act 1957

(ii) The Offences Against Person Act 1861

(iii) None. It is an offence at Common Law

43 (i) The defendant's right to call on a witness to give alibi evidence, at any stage of a trial, without giving notice to the prosecution

(ii) The defendant's right to remain silent

(iii) The defendant's right not to have any of his previous criminal record brought before the jury

44 (i) Justice

(ii) The Council for Racial Equality

(iii) The National Council for Civil Liberties

45 (i) He was a nightclub doorman
   (ii) He was a garage mechanic
   (iii) He was a TV stuntman

46 (i) He committed suicide by hanging himself
   (ii) He was beaten to death by a number of fellow prisoners
   (iii) He died during a cholera epidemic

47 (i) Because there was, at that time, no extradition treaty between Great Britain and the USA
   (ii) Because he decided to return to Britain, of his own volition, to stand trial
   (iii) Because he never left the ship and therefore, technically, had never reached the USA

48 (i) Mortuary superintendent
   (ii) City of London Beadle
   (iii) The common hangman

49 (i) It was the last public execution in England
   (ii) It was the first execution designed to break the victim's neck rather than strangle him to death
   (iii) It was the first time a priest had been hanged for murder in Britain

50 (i) He was a butler
   (ii) He was an estate manager
   (iii) He was a jobbing gardener

51 (i) Detention at His (Her) Majesty's pleasure
   (ii) Life imprisonment
   (iii) Preventive detention

52 (i) By coal gas poisoning
   (ii) By arsenic poisoning
   (iii) By neglect and starvation

53 (i) That it was used as a sexual depressant

(ii) That it was used as a cosmetic

(iii) That it was used to abort an unwanted pregnancy

54 (i) The appeal was heard after the convicted man's death at the request of his family

(ii) The Appeal Court Judges travelled, for the first time, to the scene of a crime, to see it for themselves

(iii) There is normally no opportunity for a defendant to appeal against conviction for an offence to which he has previously pleaded guilty

55 (i) *Rough Justice*

(ii) *That's Life*

(iii) *In Suspicious Circumstances*

56 (i) They were Irish

(ii) They were Norwegian

(iii) They were German

57 (i) Ronald True

(ii) Eric Rothwell Holt

(iii) Patrick Mahon

58 (i) That, in law, a person may not be put in peril twice for the same offence

(ii) That the crime was not within the court's jurisdiction

(iii) That the defendant may make a statement from the dock and is not open to cross-examination

59 (i) He attacked a bus with a sub-machine-gun

(ii) He blew up a hotel

(iii) He blew up the pier

60 (i) New York, USA

(ii) Berlin, Germany

(iii) Paris, France

Question Rating (R3)

61 (i) A pathologist, in giving evidence, produced a severed human arm for the benefit of the jury

(ii) A female volunteer was immersed in a bath of water to illustrate how the victim was murdered

(iii) An expert fired a blank cartridge from a firearm to demonstrate how much noise was emitted

62 (i) His eyes
(ii) His feet
(iii) His arms

63 (i) USA
(ii) Australia
(iii) Ireland

64 (i) A rowing boat
(ii) A horse and cart
(iii) A bicycle

65 (i) It was the first British murder trial in which, even though it was not needed, the jury could have returned a majority verdict

(ii) It was the first English murder trial presided over by a female judge

(iii) At twenty-one days it was at that time the longest murder trial of a single defendant in English legal history

66 (i) Detention at Her Majesty's pleasure
(ii) Penal servitude for life
(iii) Imprisonment for life

67 (i) A military court
(ii) An ecclesiastical court
(iii) A coroner's court

68 (i) Because he was subsequently certified insane by a panel of doctors appointed by the Home Office

(ii) Because the death penalty had been temporarily suspended in Britain

(iii) Because he was subsequently proved to have been under eighteen years of age at the time of his conviction

69 (i) London
(ii) Birmingham
(iii) York

70 (i) In the cells below the Old Bailey
(ii) Dartmoor Prison
(iii) Broadmoor Hospital

71 (i) He was a soldier
(ii) He was a policeman
(iii) He was a gamekeeper

72 (i) It was the first time that the principle was established that a defendant can only be tried once for murder

(ii) It was the first time a conviction had been set aside in a case of murder

(iii) It was the first time that a defendant was allowed to give evidence, in person, to the Court of Criminal Appeal

73 (i) 'Rebuttal of Alibi Evidence'
(ii) 'Evidence from Psychiatric Experts'
(iii) 'Evidence of System'

74 (i) Cookham Wood Prison
(ii) Rochester Prison
(iii) Canterbury Prison

75 (i) He threw water on her then pushed her against an electricity pylon

(ii) He drove his motor car at her and knocked her off her bicycle

(iii) He held her over the bridge by her feet until she was struck by a passing train

76 (i) Yugoslavia
(ii) Czechoslovakia
(iii) Bulgaria

77 (i) He had stated his familiarity with working with poison as a qualification for the post
(ii) He had written of his wife's ill health, long before she became unwell
(iii) He had described himself as a widower when his wife was still alive

78 (i) The Irish Republican Brotherhood
(ii) The Black and Tans
(iii) The Irish Republican Army

79 (i) Fighting a Japanese soldier armed with a knife
(ii) Strangling a vicious dog which was attacking him
(iii) Wringing out his washing

80 (i) J. A. Lungren
(ii) S. Morrison
(iii) S. A. Klosovski

81 (i) It was the first trial ever halted when the victim, thought to be dead, was located alive abroad
(ii) At five and a half days, it was the longest deliberation by a murder trial jury
(iii) At thirty seconds, it was the shortest British murder trial on record

82 (i) In future, the evidence of accomplices would require corroboration
(ii) In future, the evidence of accomplices would be inadmissible against a defendant in a capital murder trial
(iii) In future, evidence of an accomplice was to be given in person and not in the form of a written statement

83 (i) Rampton Hospital
(ii) Broadmoor Hospital
(iii) Bethlehem Hospital

84 (i) Because he was an American serviceman and the US authorities claimed jurisdiction in his case

(ii) Because he was a citizen of the Irish Republic who committed his crime outside England

(iii) Because he had been brought before the court after being kidnapped abroad

85 (i) The power to subpoena an unwilling witness to appear before it

(ii) The power to hear defendants in person

(iii) The power to order a new trial

86 (i) Transvestism

(ii) Sado-masochism

(iii) Sexual bondage

87 (i) The University of Kent

(ii) London University

(iii) The Open University

88 (i) Private Secretary to King George V

(ii) Commissioner of the Metropolitan Police

(iii) Chief of the Imperial General Staff

89 (i) The British Broadcasting Corporation

(ii) The Vatican

(iii) The Mafia

90 (i) It was the first occasion, in a British court, that the time of death of a victim had been scientifically calculated

(ii) It was the first time, in a British murder case, that a bullet had been scientifically proven to have been fired by a particular weapon

(iii) It was the first time in a British murder trial that bloodstains were proved to have been human

Question Rating (R4)

91 (i) Leonard Jack
Thomas
(ii) Dennis Edmund
Leckey
(iii) James Camb

92 (i) He was a surgeon
(ii) He was a dentist
(iii) He was an actor

93 (i) USA
(ii) West Germany
(iii) Spain

94 (i) Guilty but insane
(ii) Not proven
(iii) Guilty of
manslaughter

95 (i) Evidence from teeth
marks on a
discarded piece of
fruit
(ii) Evidence from
saliva on discarded
cigarette ends
(iii) Evidence from hair
samples

96 (i) Greed – they were
in debt and wanted
the victim's money
(ii) Revenge – the
victim had opposed
their marriage

(iii) Sadistic pleasure –
they wanted to
torture their victim

97 (i) Wandsworth Prison
(ii) The Theatre Royal,
Drury Lane
(iii) Lord's cricket
ground

98 (i) Because of his dual
nationality
(ii) Because of his age
(iii) Because of a
recommendation for
mercy by the jury

99 (i) 'The Doctors of
Death'
(ii) 'The Three Stooges'
(iii) 'The Three
Musketeers'

100 (i) He escaped to
Brazil and claimed
political asylum
(ii) He shot himself
dead before he
could be arrested
(iii) He was hanged for
a previous murder,
on which he was
already awaiting
execution

101 (i) 'Accidental death'
    (ii) 'Murder by Philip Yale Drew'
    (iii) 'Murder by person or persons unknown'

102 (i) They were both prizefighters
    (ii) They were both soldiers
    (iii) They were both barbers

103 (i) Because in 1931 the unsolved murder of a young woman had occurred on the Newcastle to Otterburn road – and there were similarities to Brown's crime
    (ii) Because a man who had confessed to the crime for which Brown was executed, and was not believed, lived at Otterburn
    (iii) Because 'Otterburn' turned out to be a large country house where several unidentified buried corpses were later found

104 (i) Approximately 1 per cent
    (ii) Approximately 5 per cent
    (iii) Approximately 10 per cent

105 (i) She became the first woman to lead a defence in a British murder trial
    (ii) She was the first defence counsel to withdraw from a British murder trial to give birth
    (iii) She was the first defence counsel to withdraw from a British murder trial because her client told her he was guilty

106 (i) That the representatives of any defendant, sentenced to death then found to be insane, had the choice of either removing him to an asylum for life or allowing the death penalty to be carried out

(ii) That no person who had ever been in a lunatic asylum could be sentenced to death

(iii) That a medical inquiry into the sanity of anyone sentenced to death would take place

107 (i) A cockfight
(ii) A bare knuckle fight
(iii) A duel

108 (i) Cross-examine the defendant on the whole of his past criminal record

(ii) Successfully apply to the Court of Appeal for a mistrial

(iii) To call witnesses to give hearsay evidence

109 (i) They wanted to sell his cadaver to an anatomist

(ii) They believed he was a warlock

(iii) They wanted to rob him of his clothes

110 (i) He died of a heart attack

(ii) He confessed to his brother's murder

(iii) He went mad and was sent to a lunatic asylum

111 (i) He was a short-story writer

(ii) He was a musician

(iii) He was a circus lion tamer

112 (i) He was a church warden

(ii) He was a brewer's drayman

(iii) He was a blacksmith

113 (i) He was already in prison serving a life sentence for another murder

(ii) He had already been dead for three and a half years

(iii) He had taken refuge in the Soviet Embassy in London and subsequently emigrated to the USSR

114 (i) It provided for the establishment of full-time paid cemetery attendants to guard the graves

(ii) It required written permission to be given to a doctor, by the next of kin, prior to any anatomical dissection

(iii) It repealed the law requiring every corpse to receive a Christian burial, thus allowing bodies to be donated to medical science

115 (i) The Home Office appointed a leading QC to conduct a secret inquiry into the new evidence

(ii) A new witness who had not given evidence in the original trial was heard in the Court of Criminal Appeal

(iii) The examination of *all* documents relating to a case, not just those produced at the original trial, was allowed

116 (i) It was wrapped in string and thrown into a swimming pool

(ii) It was thrown off a motorway bridge on to the fast lane below

(iii) It was left by a railway line

117 (i) That in exchange for being granted excusal from punishment the accused man agreed to study for and take Holy Orders

(ii) That any member of the clergy, including those in minor orders, came under the jurisdiction of the Church and could not be punished by any temporal court

(iii) That if the defendant could show that any member of his family line had taken Holy Orders, then he was set free

118 (i) It was the first murder prosecution instigated in Britain after the victim had been cremated

(ii) It was the first British committal proceedings on a charge of murder heard before a single stipendiary magistrate

(iii) It was the first murder prosecution to be instigated by a private individual in Britain, since 1868

119 (i) The Lebanon

(ii) Iraq

(iii) Syria

120 (i) That she was hard of hearing

(ii) That she was right handed

(iii) That she was terrified of guns

Question Rating (R5)

121 (i) Tasmania

(ii) French Guiana

(iii) French Indo-China

122 (i) 'A guilty mind'

(ii) 'A conscience'

(iii) 'Malicious jealousy'

123 (i) It was the last triple execution to be carried out at that prison

(ii) It was the first triple execution in England

(iii) It was the highest number of prisoners ever executed on a single day in Britain

124 (i) Because evidence involving the Official Secrets Acts was given

(ii) Because the proceedings took place in a prison hospital

(iii) So that the jury, at his forthcoming murder trial, would not be aware of his criminal record

125 (i) Playing with a small plastic duck

(ii) Drawing pictures of the jury

(iii) Reading a Bible

126 (i) Lord Chancellor

(ii) Ambassador to the Court of St James

(iii) Prime Minister

127 (i) David William Shaw

(ii) Peter Louis Alphon

(iii) Donald Ware

128 (i) He was shot dead by a highwayman, who robbed him of his 'blood money'

(ii) He was murdered by some of the men who had hired him in the first place

(iii) He was press-ganged into the navy while drunk and died at sea

129 (i) The Commissioner of Police of the Metropolis

(ii) The Victoria and Albert Museum

(iii) Madame Tussaud's

130 (i) Buckinghamshire

(ii) Cumbria

(iii) Cornwall

131 (i) One

(ii) None

(iii) Three

132 (i) She had hired a contract killer

(ii) She had persuaded the victim's husband to strangle his wife

(iii) She poisoned the water supply on a yacht

133 (i) He threw acid in her face

(ii) He kicked her to death

(iii) He poured petrol on her and set her alight

134 (i) More than five days

(ii) Less than five minutes

(iii) Because of the defendant's health, over five months, on and off

135 (i) He fell through the trapdoor and had to grab the legs of the condemned man to save himself

(ii) He fainted on recognizing one of the condemned men

(iii) He was dispatched to buy a Bible, which the Chaplain had forgotten to bring

136 (i) The placing of a white cap over her face

(ii) The presence of a prison chaplain

(iii) A final meal

137 (i) He threw her under a coach

(ii) He threw her from a moving train

(iii) He cut her throat

138 (i) He was the first man to hang in Armley Gaol's newly constructed execution shed

(ii) He was the first negro to be hanged in Britain

(iii) His was the last execution at Armley Gaol

139 (i) He walked into a police station and confessed

(ii) He made a confession to a priest who subsequently left the priesthood and told a policeman

(iii) An anonymous letter, naming Turner, was sent to the police by a family friend

140 (i) Shoot Furnace dead on sight

(ii) Stop every vehicle, on main roads, driving from London to the south coast

(iii) Search every garage and outbuilding in the Metropolis

141 (i) Jennifer Topped

(ii) Mary Drubbing

(iii) Fanny Adams

142 (i) He was on an LSD trip

(ii) He was on bail

(iii) He was on parole from prison

143 (i) A novel, written by him, about the capture, torture and death of a boy

(ii) A dismembered toy model of a boy

(iii) A rat crucified to a wall

144 (i) It was carried out by a female military executioner

(ii) It was the capital's largest multiple execution in over a century

(iii) It was recorded on film

145 (i) She had been bludgeoned to death with a hammer

(ii) She had been poisoned

(iii) She had been suffocated to death with a pillow

146 (i) Film of the scene of crime

(ii) The defendants' criminal records from another country

(iii) The victim's skull

147 (i) The last nobleman in England to suffer a felon's death

(ii) The last man in England to be sentenced to death by the House of Lords

(iii) The last Irish peer to be executed in England

148 (i) He hit P.C. Meehan on the head with a bottle, recklessly thrown, at a football match

(ii) He carried P.C. Meehan along the road clinging to his vehicle, until he was thrown from it and went under an oncoming car

(iii) He pushed P.C. Meehan from a rooftop while escaping from custody

149 (i) At thirty-six hours it was the shortest stay ever recorded in a British murder case. He was then hanged

(ii) At ninety-two days it was the longest stay ever recorded in a British murder case. He was then reprieved

(iii) He was the last man to occupy the death cell at Brixton Prison, London

150 (i) He tried to stab himself in the neck with a pen

(ii) He tried to gouge out his eyes

(iii) He tried to smash his skull on the dock rail

PART THREE

ANSWERS

CHAPTER ONE

ANSWERS

Question Rating (R1)

1 (iii) It was the first time a wireless telegraph had been used to effect the arrest of a murder suspect
2 (i) Not guilty
3 (iii) Her husband James
4 (ii) Arsenic
5 (i) His wife
6 (iii) Ethel le Neve
7 (ii) He was a solicitor
8 (ii) Graham Young
9 (iii) As a young boy
10 (i) Her husband
11 (ii) Belle Elmore
12 (ii) In a chocolate sweet injected with poison
13 (ii) He was American
14 (iii) The North-East
15 (ii) A nursing home
16 (ii) Dr Hawley Harvey Crippen
17 (ii) 'Killarney Kate'
18 (ii) An anonymous letter
19 (ii) Poland
20 (ii) Her husband, Frederick Bryant
21 (iii) He was French
22 (i) Classical singing
23 (iii) Scotland
24 (ii) Dr John Bodkin Adams
25 (ii) Surrey
26 (iii) His bookkeeper and secretary
27 (ii) Adelaide Bartlett
28 (iii) A court martial
29 (ii) Prostitutes
30 (i) Major

Question Rating (R2)

31 (i) It is still not known
32 (i) Less than 6 per cent
33 (i) 'The Whitechapel' murders
34 (iii) Arsenic

35 (iii) Master Sergeant

36 (iii) Dorset

37 (ii) In a public house

38 (iii) Soaking fly-papers in water

39 (iii) Brighton

40 (i) Broadmoor Hospital

41 (iii) His adulterous association with the victim's wife

42 (ii) Lincolnshire

43 (i) Arsenic

44 (i) His wife and their sons

45 (iii) Crossed eyes

46 (i) That he was accidentally poisoned by the constituents of some wallpaper in his home

47 (iii) He was a publican

48 (ii) Both were Freemasons

49 (ii) A dog

50 (ii) He was a soldier

51 (ii) That he was 'Jack the Ripper'

52 (i) Their baby son

53 (ii) Two

54 (ii) As manager of a patent-medicine company

55 (ii) He was a doctor

56 (i) Not proven

57 (i) Morphine

58 (iii) USA

59 (ii) Himself

60 (i) Arsenic

Question Rating (R3)

61 (i) He was an insurance agent

62 (ii) Antimony

63 (iii) Her sister

64 (ii) He was a doctor

65 (ii) Strychnine

66 (ii) He was a cotton broker

67 (i) Strychnine

68 (i) An associate, Reginald Parker

69 (iii) Phosphorus

70 (i) He was a male nurse

71 (i) Insanity

72 (ii) Barbiturate

73 (iii) Jersey

74 (i) SS *Montrose*

75 (iii) Neasden, London

76 (ii) A horse race meeting

77 (ii) Van Diemen's Land

78 (iii) Antimony

79 (ii) His teeth

80 (iii) Antimony

81 (iii) A bottle of bromo salts

82　(ii) His wife and mother-in-law

83　(ii) To cover up a fraudulent will

84　(ii) It allowed a defendant to be tried in London if he were unlikely to get a fair hearing in his own county

85　(iii) He was a gypsy

86　(iii) Fourteen years old

87　(i) Antimony

88　(ii) Three

89　(ii) He was a Wesleyan minister

90　(ii) In Connecticut, USA

Question Rating (R4)

91　(ii) Thallium

92　(iii) Hay-on-Wye

93　(i) Alfred Brierley

94　(iii) Strychnine

95　(ii) He was the first British poisoner known to have used thallium on his victims

96　(iii) Canada

97　(iii) Fort Leavenworth Prison, Kansas, USA

98　(ii) Because he was appalled at his wrong diagnosis, having failed to spot that she had been poisoned by morphine

99　(i) Prussic acid

100　(i) An anonymous letter to the authorities

101　(ii) Oatmeal stout

102　(iii) Paraquat

103　(ii) He was a chauffeur

104　(ii) Forgery

105　(iii) Both were Freemasons

106　(i) It was the first time the poison hyoscine was involved in a murder trial

107　(iii) Because he did not take the witness stand

108　(ii) Morphine

109　(ii) A photographic and optical equipment laboratory

110　(iii) Nitric acid

111　(ii) Forging medical prescriptions

112　(i) He was a naval sickberth attendant

113 (i) He was a teacher

114 (ii) He had taken his own life with the same poison

115 (ii) Phosphorus

116 (ii) A chemistry set

117 (ii) Hull

118 (ii) To get married

119 (iii) Morphine

120 (ii) Alice Yapp

Question Rating (R5)

121 (ii) Her husband, Michael Barber

122 (i) His landlady Mrs Blume, who had been tricked into signing a will in his favour

123 (ii) 'J. Wanker'

124 (iii) He was a jobbing gardener

125 (i) The lighthouse at Margate

126 (ii) Because she had syphilis

127 (ii) Ten to twenty victims

128 (ii) Insulin

129 (i) He was an insurance salesman

130 (ii) Opium

131 (iii) Thirteen or fourteen

132 (i) Discrepancies in scientific, analytical tests

133 (i) A poisoned chocolate cream

134 (iii) Cornwall

135 (iii) 'The Bovingdon Bug'

136 (i) France

137 (ii) Half the steel part of his spectacles

138 (iii) He was a doctor

139 (iii) Cornwall

140 (ii) He became the only solicitor ever to be hanged for murder

141 (ii) It was the last public hanging in Scotland

142 (i) That letters and a photograph of his mistress be buried with him

143 (i) His mother-in-law

144 (iii) Arsenic

145 (i) Her father

146 (ii) Cyanide

147 (i) It was the first time that this charge had been preferred as a result of evidence from a cremated corpse

148 (i) *My Fifteen Lost Years*

149 (i) It was the first recorded charge of murder using liquid chloroform

150 (ii) The Central Criminal Court

CHAPTER TWO

ANSWERS

Question Rating (R1)

1 (iii) Asphyxiation
2 (ii) 10 Rillington Place
3 (iii) Glasgow
4 (ii) Husband and wife
5 (ii) To a woman who died over 1500 years ago
6 (iii) John Christie
7 (ii) His wife
8 (ii) Scotland
9 (iii) His wife
10 (i) A gold chain belonging to the victim and found at his lodgings
11 (iii) Chinese
12 (ii) He was homosexual
13 (iii) Birmingham
14 (ii) Life imprisonment
15 (i) By fire
16 (i) Edward Marshall Hall
17 (iii) Cyprus
18 (ii) An overcoat button
19 (i) Amelia Dyer
20 (ii) India
21 (ii) His habit of quoting from the Bible
22 (iii) Australia
23 (i) Police questioning of suspects and, in particular, of children and the educationally subnormal
24 (ii) A sexual assault
25 (ii) Two
26 (iii) They were all infants or children
27 (i) American
28 (ii) Soot. (The murderer had started a fire to make it look as if she had died by smoke inhalation and asphyxia – in which case there would have been soot in her lungs)
29 (iii) His hands
30 (ii) Sister-in-law

Question Rating (R2)

31	(iii)	On a cart
32	(i)	Rape
33	(i)	Sir Bernard Spilsbury
34	(i)	Dental work
35	(iii)	A YWCA hostel
36	(i)	It was never discovered
37	(ii)	Nottinghamshire
38	(i)	A silk scarf
39	(ii)	Hove, Sussex
40	(ii)	An artist
41	(ii)	Not guilty
42	(i)	They were mother-in-law and daughter-in-law
43	(i)	His daughter, Geraldine
44	(iii)	Laundry marks on clothing
45	(ii)	A posthumous free pardon
46	(iii)	The British Broadcasting Corporation
47	(iii)	Comparison of the skulls with known photographs
48	(i)	Liverpool
49	(iii)	Hypnosis
50	(iii)	The Royal Air Force
51	(i)	By setting fire to it
52	(iii)	His mother
53	(iii)	Northamptonshire
54	(ii)	Footprints
55	(iii)	Bedfordshire
56	(i)	She set fire to it
57	(i)	His hands
58	(ii)	The hyoid bone
59	(iii)	Spain
60	(iii)	Forensic evidence

Question Rating (R3)

61 (ii) A note scrawled in ballpoint pen (saying 'This was the thing I thought would never come')

62 (i) The Royal Navy

63 (i) A police cell in Clapham, London

64 (ii) Because of Rouse's confession, later published in the *Daily Sketch*

65 (ii) A bootlace

66 (i) The fact that she was infertile

67 (ii) He was a hotel barman

68 (iii) Identification by dental bite marks on the victim

69 (ii) The Metropole Hotel

70 (iii) She was his fiancée

71 (ii) German

72 (i) Insanity

73 (iii) Her victim's scarf

74 (ii) That he had killed in his sleep, therefore no crime had been committed

75 (iii) She was his common-law wife

76 (ii) A ballroom

77 (i) They were both carried out by Dr Keith Simpson

78 (iii) A ligature

79 (ii) Because he was a spy

80 (iii) One day and a half

81 (ii) A suspicion of infidelity on the part of his common-law wife

82 (i) Fingerprints

83 (ii) Vauxhall

84 (iii) Because he had undressed first

85 (i) Surrey

86 (iii) A request for his fingerprints

87 (i) The victim's body had not been found and there was insufficient evidence for a charge of murder

88 (i) Guilty of manslaughter

89 (iii) His socks and shoelaces

90 (ii) He was a fashion shop manager

Question Rating (R4)

91 (iii) A married man
92 (ii) The Leicestershire Regiment
93 (ii) An approved school
94 (i) Lancaster
95 (i) Parkinson's disease
96 (ii) Field made a confession to a newspaper
97 (iii) Not guilty
98 (ii) Make an appeal
99 (ii) An unfinished portrait of her
100 (i) His dog
101 (ii) He was a van driver
102 (i) In a river
103 (i) They were searching for a missing foreign tourist
104 (ii) Three
105 (ii) He was a lorry driver and motor mechanic
106 (i) 'The John Barleycorn'
107 (i) Life imprisonment
108 (ii) It was the Old Bailey's first murder trial of the twentieth century
109 (iii) USA
110 (iii) Rape

111 (iii) That known sex offenders be kept under stricter control
112 (iii) South Africa
113 (i) She had been a cinema attendant
114 (i) The flagstaff bearing the black flag snapped
115 (iii) Unlawfully obtaining credit
116 (iii) The Royal Army Medical Corps
117 (iii) Strangeways Prison
118 (i) Libel proceedings
119 (ii) He was a policeman
120 (ii) The USA

Question Rating (R5)

121 (i) The death sentence
122 (ii) In the cellar beneath the murderer's flat
123 (iii) Forty years
124 (ii) A prostitute
125 (i) Ypres
126 (iii) A piece of clothes line
127 (ii) He was a labourer in a quarry
128 (ii) A blazing torch was rammed down the victim's throat
129 (ii) Blue serge

130 (ii) Pieces of tape

131 (i) Guilty of manslaughter

132 (ii) Blind cord

133 (iii) The defendant's own confession to a newspaper

134 (i) A table knife

135 (ii) *Sunday Graphic*

136 (iii) A mutilated hand

137 (ii) A man's woollen vest

138 (iii) Tuberculosis

139 (ii) Falsely obtaining money due to the victim under a court order

140 (ii) A cleaning solution

141 (i) His hands

142 (iii) 'Thunder Thighs'

143 (ii) A box of face powder

144 (iii) A silk scarf

145 (ii) Nine

146 (ii) *News of the World*

147 (i) Theft of jewellery

148 (iii) *People*

149 (ii) He was freed on appeal

150 (iii) A note confessing his guilt

CHAPTER THREE

ANSWERS

Question Rating (R1)

1   (iii) It was the last hanging of a woman in Britain
2   (ii) Derek Bentley
3   (ii) Hungerford
4   (ii) The A6
5   (i) Michael Ryan
6   (i) He set fire to it
7   (ii) Maria Marten
8   (ii) Chinese
9   (iii) Fog
10   (iii) It has no grooves
11   (ii) George Ince
12   (iii) After a villa in which the shooting occurred
13   (iii) His eyes
14   (ii) He was a racing-car driver
15   (i) German
16   (i) Christopher Craig
17   (iii) He was a policeman
18   (iii) 'Deadman's Hill'
19   (i) Egyptian
20   (iii) He had jumped from a roof
21   (iii) Northumberland
22   (iii) British
23   (iii) William Corder
24   (i) She was a night club manageress
25   (i) He was a soldier
26   (ii) Valerie Storie
27   (i) American
28   (i) Buried in the ground
29   (i) Robbery
30   (ii) Striation marks

Question Rating (R2)

31   (iii) 'Red Max'
32   (iii) As a groom
33   (i) They were fired from two different guns
34   (ii) Essex
35   (ii) On a London bus
36   (ii) French
37   (iii) Croydon, Surrey

38 (i) Cartridge cases from the murder weapon

39 (iii) A sawn-off shotgun

40 (ii) He was a policeman

41 (iii) Lancashire

42 (iii) He was shot while trying to foil the escape of a number of robbers

43 (ii) Canada

44 (i) He was a soldier

45 (iii) A motor cycle

46 (i) 'The Cleft Chin Murder'

47 (iii) He was a policeman

48 (i) In a well

49 (ii) He committed suicide

50 (ii) On a railway train

51 (iii) He was a tailor

52 (ii) They were friends and business partners

53 (i) He was recognized as a former policeman

54 (i) Cheshire

55 (i) Polstead, Suffolk

56 (iii) The comparison microscope

57 (iii) Essex

58 (ii) Kent

59 (ii) They were in a stolen car

60 (iii) Polish

Question Rating (R3)

61 (ii) Icy blue eyes

62 (i) Yorkshire

63 (ii) Sixteen and nineteen

64 (ii) She was a striptease dancer

65 (ii) He wanted to fake his own suicide

66 (iii) He was a policeman

67 (ii) Fog and mist

68 (iii) The victim's mother had a dream about the location of the body

69 (i) Blackpool

70 (ii) A pistol

71 (iii) He was a research scientist

72 (iii) Glasgow

73 (i) The Royal Engineers

74 (i) A Smith and Wesson

75 (iii) She was a housekeeper

76 (ii) Canada

77 (iii) Webley

78 (ii) Barclays Bank

79 (iii) He was a deserter from the army

80 (ii) A bank robbery

81 (ii) Captain

82 (i) A jeweller's shop

83 (iii) 'Scottie'

84 (i) Essex

85 (i) An army truck

86 (iii) Surrey

87 (iii) Her husband's

88 (i) He was a builder

89 (ii) In a bath in the kitchen

90 (ii) That they were father and son

Question Rating (R4)

91 (ii) He was an auctioneer and surveyor

92 (i) He said that she had committed suicide with the gun

93 (i) A car

94 (i) They were policemen

95 (i) Eton College

96 (i) He was a garage mechanic

97 (iii) He was a dock worker

98 (i) He was making a blackmail telephone call which was traced by the police

99 (ii) A colliery

100 (i) In the victim's notebook

101 (ii) Hampshire

102 (ii) Because Dyer was already dead by then

103 (iii) Britain's first department store

104 (ii) A shotgun

105 (ii) A bank

106 (ii) Devil's Island

107 (ii) About four years

108 (ii) Three

109 (i) The London Docks

110 (iii) 'The Hooded Man'

111 (i) The victim's mother had a dream which accurately located the body of her dead son

112 (i) Southend-on-Sea, Essex

113 (iii) That she was pregnant

114 (i) Both witnesses failed to identify him on an identity parade

115 (i) They were landlord and tenant

116 (ii) Circumstantial evidence

117 (iii) A wide-brimmed hat

118 (ii) His head was severely injured in a fight

119 (iii) Mrs Muriel Patience at the 'Barn Restaurant'

120 (i) Derham was in love with Smith's wife

Question Rating (R5)

121 (i) He was in prison
122 (i) They were both deserters
123 (iii) He had been a dentist
124 (ii) A Smith and Wesson
125 (iii) Norfolk
126 (i) France
127 (i) He was a motor-cycle repair shop owner
128 (ii) At a local hospital
129 (ii) He was a brewer
130 (ii) Cambridgeshire
131 (iii) He was a painter
132 (ii) A 'health order'
133 (ii) Cobb prised some bullets from a tree, which had been used by the murderer for 'practice' shots, for ballistic comparison

134 (i) There were three bullet wounds in her back
135 (ii) 'Russian Robert'
136 (ii) A bullet previously fired from a gun by Clarke was removed from the ceiling of a house and found to match the murder bullets
137 (i) He was in the Merchant Navy
138 (ii) A chapel
139 (iii) He was a journalist
140 (ii) Arranging marriage ceremonies for women wanting British citizenship
141 (iii) 'The Welcomes'
142 (i) Yorkshire
143 (iii) A revolver
144 (ii) George MacKay
145 (ii) A Luger
146 (ii) Two
147 (ii) They were policemen
148 (iii) A Webley
149 (i) Nantwich, Cheshire
150 (iii) He was a poultry farmer

CHAPTER FOUR

ANSWERS

Question Rating (R1)

1	(iii)	Joe Orton
2	(ii)	Liverpool
3	(i)	On Clapham Common
4	(ii)	He was German
5	(ii)	'Murder by Lord Lucan'
6	(iii)	He was an insurance agent
7	(iii)	Glasgow
8	(iii)	Russian
9	(iii)	A hotel
10	(iii)	He was a chicken farmer
11	(i)	Prudential Assurance
12	(i)	He had dismembered her body
13	(i)	'Bill', because she was a lesbian
14	(ii)	London
15	(iii)	She was a prostitute
16	(i)	A cloakroom ticket
17	(i)	Edinburgh
18	(iii)	'Bertie' Manton
19	(ii)	New York, USA
20	(iii)	A lantern. (One of the defendant's brothers-in-law identified it as belonging to the murderer)
21	(ii)	In a rented bungalow
22	(ii)	Sussex
23	(ii)	He was German
24	(i)	Inside a sack
25	(ii)	A shape like the letter 'S' was cut into each cheek

26 (ii) Sir Arthur Conan Doyle
27 (ii) Southampton
28 (i) She was a children's nanny
29 (iii) The first murder on a train
30 (ii) He was a pantry boy

Question Rating (R2)

31 (i) His pregnant wife, Ruby
32 (ii) Oxford
33 (iii) A chess club
34 (i) Major
35 (ii) Waterloo Station, London
36 (i) Eighteen years old
37 (i) In a river
38 (i) Robbery
39 (iii) She dressed in men's clothing
40 (ii) The lock of a canal
41 (iii) USA
42 (iii) He was a landlord
43 (iii) An oil company depot
44 (iii) Bournemouth
45 (ii) Jealousy. The murderer was the victim's wife's lover
46 (i) A type of hat
47 (ii) 'The Crumbles'
48 (iii) Morphia

49 (ii) He said that she had accidentally hit her head on a coal scuttle during a fight with him
50 (i) She was a typist
51 (i) London
52 (ii) A rolling pin
53 (ii) He had been a salesman
54 (ii) He was a driver for the National Fire Service
55 (i) The Isle of Arran
56 (iii) He was a tailor
57 (ii) A public house
58 (i) A walking stick
59 (i) In Scotland
60 (ii) They were discovered, by the victim, during a burglary

Question Rating (R3)

61 (i) The Royal Flying Corps
62 (iii) He was a soda fountain salesman
63 (ii) A hammer
64 (iii) 'The Luton Sack Murder'
65 (iii) She was an unemployed typist

66 (ii) He was a
professional burglar
67 (iii) 'Pigsticker'
68 (i) A Palace of
Varieties
69 (ii) They were casual
labourers
70 (ii) He wanted to avoid
marriage to his
victim. (She had told
him (untruthfully)
that she was
pregnant)
71 (ii) He was a tarpaulin
packer
72 (i) A revolver
73 (i) As a chauffeur/
handyman
74 (i) A cook's knife and a
meat saw
75 (ii) A refuse tip
76 (i) She was a
shorthand typist and
bookkeeper
77 (i) A hammer
78 (i) She had been a bus
conductress
79 (iii) The beam showed
no marks from the
cord supposedly
used
80 (i) 'Moosh' and 'Tiggy'
81 (ii) Lancashire
82 (iii) He had driven over
her, repeatedly, with
a car

83 (i) He was a taxi driver
84 (ii) He was a Turkish
Cypriot
85 (ii) They were one and
the same person
86 (iii) Sussex
87 (iii) With a wooden stool
88 (iii) A handcart
89 (iii) A car jack
90 (iii) He was a prison
officer

Question Rating (R4)

91 (i) Yorkshire
92 (i) His second wife
93 (ii) He was an architect
94 (iii) His visiting card
95 (iii) A pawnbroker's
shop
96 (ii) He was a policeman
97 (iii) Yorkshire
98 (ii) Edinburgh
99 (ii) A blow across the
throat (possibly a
karate chop)
100 (i) The cinema
101 (ii) She was Belgian
102 (i) He was a
headmaster
103 (ii) Black satin
104 (iii) An axe
105 (iii) In a shop
106 (i) A hammer

107 (ii) In police custody for another offence

108 (i) His mis-spelling of a word which matched a similar mis-spelling in letters he purported to have received from his wife but which were dated after her death

109 (iii) A hammer

110 (i) He had been a boxer

111 (i) A bowler hat

112 (i) The victim had stolen food from them

113 (ii) On his bicycle

114 (ii) He was a motor mechanic

115 (ii) Oxfordshire

116 (ii) He was a soldier

117 (i) The drug, cocaine

118 (iii) The victim had discovered that the murderer was committing fraud

119 (ii) Her boots

120 (iii) In a mineshaft

Question Rating (R5)

121 (ii) Patrick Mahon

122 (i) 'One Minute Michaelson'

123 (iii) He was a tennis coach

124 (ii) A tubular steel chair

125 (ii) Guilty of manslaughter (not guilty of murder)

126 (iii) She had been pushed from her bedroom window

127 (ii) A mallet

128 (ii) Staffordshire

129 (ii) She was pretending to her husband that she was at her sister's home 'in confinement', prior to having a baby. (He had only married her because she told him, untruthfully, that she was pregnant)

130 (ii) They were elephant keepers

131 (ii) A poker

132 (iii) He claimed it was a road traffic accident

133 (i) As a chauffeur

134 (i) Yorkshire

135 (ii) An iron golf tee marker

136 (i) He was a lorry driver

137 (i) On a mountain

138 (iii) A palm print

139 (i) As a cook

140 (ii) A flat iron

141 (i) Paris

142 (ii) 'Qualtrough'

143 (i) Fifteen years old

144 (ii) A hammer

145 (iii) 25 Menlove Gardens East, Mossley Hill

146 (i) A pistol

147 (i) He said it was a road accident, with the car hitting a tree

148 (ii) In a pram

149 (i) On a golf course

150 (ii) Leschziner

CHAPTER FIVE

ANSWERS

Question Rating (R1)

1   (iii) He was a policeman
2   (iii) The majority
3   (i)   Oscar Wilde
4   (ii) Incised wounds and stab wounds
5   (iii) The Identikit system
6   (i)   He was Swiss
7   (ii) Durham
8   (iii) Robert Fabian
9   (iii) He was a soldier
10 (i)   The Broadwater Farm Estate
11 (i)   The House of Lords
12 (iii) They were homosexual lovers
13 (i)   American
14 (i)   Painting
15 (i)   They formed a 'Defence Committee' for the convicted man
16 (i)   Glasgow
17 (iii) She was a prostitute
18 (iii) Cheshire
19 (iii) He was Turkish
20 (ii) He gave himself up to the police and confessed
21 (iii) He was an actor
22 (ii) Kent
23 (i)   He was an actor
24 (iii) His daughter
25 (iii) The Army
26 (ii) It had been thrown from an aircraft
27 (ii) He was a police officer
28 (i)   Percy Thompson, his lover's husband
29 (ii) Gretna Green
30 (ii) 'The Rising Sun'

Question Rating (R2)

31 (iii) Edith Thompson
32 (i)   To have sexual intercourse

33 (ii) No one was ever convicted

34 (ii) Robert Wood

35 (ii) He was a bus conductor

36 (ii) A fictional crime story which contained details of the real murder

37 (i) Following his release in 1958 he made a confession, published in a newspaper

38 (iii) He was a merchant seaman

39 (ii) An antique shop

40 (ii) Jealousy – the murderer was having an affair with the victim's husband

41 (i) He was a labourer

42 (ii) London

43 (ii) She was a prostitute

44 (iii) *Mayfair* magazine

45 (ii) He was Italian

46 (ii) Essex

47 (ii) She was a prostitute

48 (ii) John Lee

49 (ii) Essex

50 (i) Jealousy – she was having an affair with a man at a nearby love-nest

51 (i) 'Nicky the Greek'

52 (iii) Kent

53 (ii) None

54 (i) Staffordshire

55 (i) None

56 (ii) The anti-nuclear movement

57 (i) A railway carriage

58 (iii) The Royal Air Force

59 (i) Essex

60 (i) Because the defendant was drunk and believed his victim to be a dummy

Question Rating (R3)

61 (ii) Scotland

62 (i) Dismemberment of one who has disgraced their family then sending the parts on trains heading in different directions

63 (iii) Gunner

64 (i) USA

65 (ii) Another man confessed to the earlier killing

66 (ii) The P & O Line

67 (ii) She was Irish

68 (ii) BBC radio broadcasts

69 (ii) With a Japanese samurai sword

70 (iii) Tuberculosis

71 (i) He was a stockbroker

72 (iii) Cumbria

73 (i) He was dead from natural causes

74 (i) He had been a railway engine driver

75 (iii) He was a Barbadian

76 (ii) She was a prostitute

77 (iii) He was the hangman's assistant at the murderer's execution

78 (ii) Mrs Cynthia Jarrett

79 (iii) Workington, Cumbria

80 (i) None

81 (iii) Wimbledon

82 (i) He gave himself up to the police

83 (ii) Lancashire

84 (ii) He was a gardener

85 (iii) On Dartford Heath

86 (iii) The Devil's Punch Bowl

87 (ii) He was having a homosexual affair with a hotel worker

88 (i) It was a superstition that the corpse would bleed when touched by its killer

89 (ii) The Navy

90 (ii) A hay fork

Question Rating (R4)

91 (i) 'Smiler'

92 (ii) He was smuggling drugs

93 (ii) The victim was apparently still alive at the time

94 (ii) A table knife

95 (i) A dance-hall

96 (ii) She was a prostitute

97 (i) A public house

98 (ii) They were dairymen

99 (iii) Manchester

100 (ii) He was a sailor

101 (iii) Austria

102 (iii) Sheffield

103 (iii) He was French

104 (ii) Camberwell

105 (ii) A mill and a building contractor's business

106 (i) Twenty-four hours

107 (i) For being an accessory to the crime

108 (iii) Self-defence

109 (ii) As a manservant

110 (i) She was Polish

111 (ii) Her four-year-old son

112 (ii) Switzerland

113 (i) He pleaded insanity
114 (i) He was an art student
115 (ii) The assassination of the entire Cabinet
116 (iii) His tiny feet
117 (ii) Television
118 (iii) 'Phyllis'
119 (i) A public house
120 (i) She was a milliner's assistant

Question Rating (R5)

121 (ii) A bowler hat
122 (iii) A dagger
123 (ii) Cornwall
124 (i) He was a shipping clerk
125 (i) As a result of a road traffic accident. (The police attended the scene, searched his vehicle and found human remains)
126 (iii) She had been a British Intelligence Agent
127 (iii) A clasp knife
128 (iii) In a school
129 (ii) Esperanto
130 (i) In a drinking club
131 (ii) He was a laundry van driver

132 (i) Wounding with intent to murder the same victim, his wife
133 (ii) Robbery – he was out of work
134 (iii) A razor
135 (i) He was a journalist
136 (ii) Liverpool
137 (i) An engraved watch
138 (i) He was facing extradition to serve a prison sentence for a previous murder and she had begun divorce proceedings
139 (ii) He was a newspaper warehouseman
140 (i) A tradesman's van
141 (ii) He was a scaffolder
142 (ii) She was a *Playboy* Bunny Girl
143 (iii) In a multi-storey car park
144 (ii) Because he was a man with a history of violence against her and had tried to strangle her
145 (ii) Norfolk
146 (ii) A cleaver
147 (iii) Jealousy – he thought his wife was having a love affair

148 (i) Norfolk

149 (i) He was a ship's
            steward

150 (iii) He had deserted
            from the forces in
            the First World War

CHAPTER SIX

ANSWERS

Question Rating (R1)

1	(ii)	They all had their throats cut
2	(ii)	'The Yorkshire Ripper'
3	(ii)	'The Black Panther'
4	(iii)	They were all prostitutes
5	(iii)	Boxing
6	(i)	Lesley Whittle
7	(iii)	He drowned them in a bath
8	(ii)	'The Acid Bath Murderer'
9	(iii)	Three
10	(ii)	Ronald, Reginald and Charles
11	(iii)	He was a civil servant
12	(ii)	Three
13	(ii)	'The Brides in the Bath Murderer'
14	(ii)	Once
15	(ii)	'The Richardson gang'
16	(ii)	Five
17	(i)	Edward Marshall Hall
18	(i)	She was killed in a room
19	(iii)	The black hood which he wore when committing robberies
20	(ii)	Three
21	(ii)	Cornwall
22	(ii)	He drank fresh blood from the corpses
23	(iii)	The Duke of Clarence
24	(ii)	They were prostitutes
25	(ii)	A Geordie accent
26	(iii)	Ronald
27	(i)	Most were strangled
28	(iii)	Wormwood Scrubs
29	(iii)	Half a kidney from a female victim
30	(ii)	The City of London Force

Question Rating (R2)

31 (i) She was a prostitute
32 (ii) Edinburgh
33 (iii) He was unusually short (5' 4") and bow-legged
34 (iii) Gravesend
35 (i) They were all sub-postmasters
36 (i) They were all his bigamous wives
37 (ii) Charles Frederick Peace
38 (iii) Sulphuric acid
39 (iii) Seven
40 (ii) He strangled them
41 (iii) They were both prostitutes
42 (ii) 'Dark Annie'
43 (i) A gun
44 (ii) The Royal Air Force
45 (iii) They were all shot dead
46 (ii) Sonia Sutcliffe
47 (iii) France
48 (ii) He was shot in the head
49 (ii) In Scotland
50 (ii) Frank Mitchell
51 (iii) Because he was a homosexual
52 (iii) 'Jack the Hat'
53 (i) The Royal Air Force
54 (ii) On a bomb site
55 (iii) He was a long-distance lorry driver
56 (iii) Violet
57 (iii) A service issue gas mask
58 (i) He was stabbed to death with a carving knife
59 (ii) 'The Firm'
60 (ii) Rugby School

Question Rating (R3)

61 (iii) A man in custody for another offence confessed to the murder
62 (iii) Superintendent Tommy Butler
63 (iii) In a field near a farm
64 (i) In bed
65 (iii) Manchester
66 (iii) Adolf Hitler
67 (i) Czechoslovakia
68 (ii) In a wood in North Wales
69 (iii) Yorkshire
70 (ii) He was a joiner
71 (i) Australia

72 (i) He confessed to both murders. (The judge directed the jury to acquit him on the first occasion due to inconsistencies in the evidence with the true facts of the murder)

73 (i) Hull

74 (i) One

75 (i) He shot her in the neck

76 (i) A disused aircraft hangar at the edge of a wood

77 (iii) The Royal Fusiliers

78 (i) He shot them both with a revolver

79 (ii) Dr Crippen

80 (iii) A suicide pact

81 (iii) 'Long Liz'

82 (i) Wales

83 (i) He had beaten her to death with a hammer

84 (iii) Glasgow

85 (ii) He was a solicitor

86 (ii) Four

87 (i) Bethnal Green

88 (iii) He had been a policeman

89 (ii) Yorkshire

90 (iii) He was clerk to the Magistrates in the court where his son was charged with his murder

Question Rating (R4)

91 (iii) 'The Man Who Talked Too Much'

92 (iii) A blue Standard Vanguard Estate

93 (ii) They died as a result of an arson attack

94 (iii) Kent

95 (iii) The corpse had gallstones – and Moseley was known to suffer from them

96 (ii) John Duddy

97 (i) 'The Fort'

98 (i) Six

99 (iii) A hammer

100 (ii) His daughter

101 (iii) Thirteen

102 (i) Hampshire

103 (ii) Following his face being slashed with a razor by a fellow inmate

104 (ii) An Alvis

105 (ii) Strong left-wing political sympathies

106 (ii) He was interviewed, sitting in a car with a prostitute, by vice-squad officers

107 (ii) Liverpool

108 (iii) He was a fisherman

109 (ii) By a shotgun

110 (iii) A rolling pin

111 (ii) He stabbed them to death

112 (i) He was stopped in the street by police officers suspicious of his movements

113 (iii) At the foot of some cliffs on a beach

114 (ii) Jealousy – he wished to have an affair with Dyson's wife

115 (i) One

116 (iii) 'The Double R'

117 (ii) He stabbed them all

118 (ii) 'Foxtrot One One'

119 (ii) They had cotton threads across gaps in the hedges which he broke when inspecting the graves at night

120 (i) Sir Charles Warren

Question Rating (R5)

121 (i) She committed suicide

122 (ii) Donald Nappey

123 (ii) The Northamptonshire Regiment

124 (iii) The manufacture of artificial fingernails

125 (ii) Ice-cream vans

126 (ii) The Plymouth Brethren

127 (i) Geoffrey Fox, Christopher Head and David Wombwell

128 (ii) Six

129 (iii) In a wheelbarrow

130 (ii) Duddy and Witney

131 (ii) A tin opener

132 (i) In a public convenience

133 (ii) Austria

134 (iii) Fifteen

135 (i) Esmeralda's Barn

136 (iii) Hampshire

137 (i) He believed that she had infected him with venereal disease

138 (iii) He stabbed them both with a knife and hit the mother with an axe

139 (i) By strangulation

140 (ii) Peter Fell himself

141 (ii) In a wood

142 (i) His wife and four children

143 (ii) France

144 (ii) He was a driving instructor

145 (ii) The Royal Corps of Transport

146 (ii) Four

147 (iii) He left a note with his clothes, on a beach, suggesting he had committed suicide

148 (ii) Sixteen

149 (iii) Because the blood found on the murder weapon was mostly his, indicating that his wound had been inflicted last

150 (iii) He was a labourer

CHAPTER SEVEN

ANSWERS

Question Rating (R1)

1   (iii) Ian Brady and Myra Hindley
2   (iii) She was a nurse
3   (iii) DNA fingerprinting
4   (ii) It has never been established
5   (iii) She was a baby farmer
6   (ii) He was a necrophiliac
7   (i) Newcastle
8   (ii) Saddleworth Moors
9   (iii) Sir Richard Attenborough
10 (ii) Neville George Clevely Heath
11 (ii) He bludgeoned her to death with a car spanner
12 (ii) Lord Longford
13 (iii) Broadmoor Hospital
14 (iii) Glasgow
15 (i) Nobody
16 (i) Irish
17 (iii) Maxwell Confait
18 (ii) London
19 (i) Samples of female pubic hair
20 (ii) A chemicals firm
21 (iii) By using coal gas
22 (iii) A War Reserve policeman
23 (ii) Eleven years old
24 (iii) Wales
25 (ii) Halifax, Yorkshire
26 (i) Manchester
27 (i) 'The Stockwell Strangler'
28 (iii) Psychological offender profiling
29 (ii) Male homosexuals
30 (ii) He was on his newspaper round

Question Rating (R2)

31 (i) South Africa
32 (i) He was strangled
33 (ii) Nazi

34 (i) The 'Railway Killer'

35 (i) He was shot in the head

36 (iii) 'The Wolf Man'

37 (ii) He was a chauffeur

38 (i) In a disused coalmine

39 (iii) He was bludgeoned to death with an axe

40 (iii) 'In the circumstances, you might make that a double!'

41 (ii) An axe

42 (i) The Royal Air Force

43 (ii) Fifteen years old

44 (i) They were stabbed to death

45 (ii) Halifax, Yorkshire

46 (iii) Two women who were opening a children's home

47 (iii) She had been neglected and starved to death

48 (iii) He was a church caretaker

49 (ii) He was strangled

50 (iii) A leather riding whip

51 (ii) Elderly men and women

52 (iii) Attempted rape

53 (iii) Italy

54 (ii) He was her stepfather

55 (i) 'The Carbon Copy Murders'

56 (ii) They were both teachers

57 (iii) They disposed of other women's unwanted babies

58 (ii) Four

59 (iii) Her head was smashed against a wall

60 (iii) Six

Question Rating (R3)

61 (iii) The Royal Army Service Corps

62 (i) The weapon was taken home, for his own use, by a policeman who found it in a police car

63 (ii) Suffolk

64 (i) Two

65 (iii) Buckinghamshire

66 (i) A women's lavatory at a railway station

67 (ii) They were all strangled

68 (iii) Hungtingdonshire

69 (i) She strangled him

70 (i) Four

71 (ii) He stabbed her to death

72 (iii) Seven

73 (iii) Fear – he believed she would give evidence against him for sexually abusing her

74 (i) She was his half-sister

75 (i) Three

76 (ii) They were both homosexuals

77 (ii) They all contained significant spelling errors

78 (iii) An axe

79 (ii) They fingerprinted every male over the age of sixteen believed possibly to have been in the vicinity of the scene of crime at the relevant time

80 (ii) Surrey

81 (i) Lesley Ann Downey

82 (iii) He was a lorry driver

83 (i) She was a typist

84 (i) A pilot

85 (ii) He was a stock clerk

86 (i) She believed she was possessed by an evil voodoo spirit

87 (ii) 'Reggie-no-dick'

88 (iii) Derbyshire

89 (i) He used a ladder placed on a fire escape and entered his room through a window

90 (ii) He received an anonymous letter, which was proved to have been written by Heys, containing incriminating information

Question Rating (R4)

91 (ii) Group Captain Rupert Brooke

92 (iii) He claimed to have killed while suffering a nightmare in his sleep

93 (iii) She was suffocated

94 (i) The Welsh Guards

95 (iii) He was a builder's labourer

96 (i) The murders of two other children

97 (ii) Guildford, Surrey

98 (ii) Approximately two years

99 (i) Norma Joyce Bell

100 (ii) A seed merchant

101 (i) The Royal Artillery

102 (iii) In France during the First World War

103 (ii) He had been suffocated

104 (ii) He worked in a brickworks

105 (i) Rampton Hospital

106 (iii) Dog hairs

107 (i) He was delivering a newspaper on his round

108 (i) She was a children's governess

109 (ii) He pleaded that there had been a suicide pact with his wife

110 (ii) David Smith

111 (i) A hammer

112 (ii) Cheshire

113 (ii) Sado-homosexual characteristics

114 (iii) She was strangled with her own tights

115 (i) Wiltshire

116 (iii) She was suffocated

117 (i) Essex

118 (ii) He stabbed them to death

119 (i) Yorkshire

120 (ii) He was a soldier

Question Rating (R5)

121 (i) Worcestershire

122 (i) In a public house

123 (i) He had been an assistant chef

124 (iii) In a divan base in the home

125 (ii) She was sixteen years old

126 (iii) She was a midwife

127 (iii) She drowned her in a cesspool

128 (ii) Her own child

129 (i) He was a packer in a flour mill

130 (i) Four

131 (iii) Keith Bennett

132 (iii) He was four years old

133 (ii) The Royal Air Force

134 (ii) The Duke of Kent

135 (i) He garrotted them

136 (iii) He was a deputy inspector of factories

137 (i) Three

138 (ii) A bubble car

139 (ii) 'Evidence of System' (i.e. previous poisonings)

140 (i) Bath

141 (i) Two

142 (iii) A prayer book

143 (i) He was a building site labourer

144 (i) He was French

145 (ii) Munchausen Syndrome

146 (ii) Brighton, Sussex

147 (iii) Neville George
Clevely Heath

148 (ii) A bottle top

149 (iii) George Sanders

150 (iii) He suffocated her
by wrapping
clingfilm around her
face

CHAPTER EIGHT

ANSWERS

Question Rating (R1)

1 (ii) John Reginald Halliday Christie

2 (iii) Whitechapel

3 (ii) On the ramp of the House of Commons underground car park

4 (ii) 'The Blind Beggar'

5 (iii) Edinburgh

6 (ii) A public house

7 (i) Under the cellar floor

8 (i) 'The Ratcliffe Highway Murders'

9 (ii) In the House of Commons, Westminster

10 (ii) Mrs Muriel McKay

11 (ii) On the roof of a warehouse

12 (ii) It burned to the ground

13 (iii) 10 Rillington Place, W11

14 (iii) Glasgow

15 (ii) On the beach

16 (iii) Rigor mortis

17 (iii) The Grand Hotel

18 (i) Hanging from the north arch of Blackfriars Bridge

19 (ii) He shot him in the head with a revolver

20 (i) By a palm print

21 (iii) Libya's

22 (iii) Sir Robert Peel's

23 (ii) Lyons Corner House

24 (i) 'The Murder Bag'

25 (iii) In a peat bog

26 (ii) It was never found

27 (iii) Powder burns

28 (ii) Lincolnshire

29 (ii) Waterloo Bridge

30 (i) Essex

Question Rating (R2)

31 (iii) They were the same building, Lancaster Castle

32 (iii) A hospital

33 (ii) An anti-tank mine

34 (ii) In a car

35 (iii) In a sewage tunnel

36 (iii) The Hosein brothers

37 (iii) On a train

38 (ii) Dennis Nilsen

39 (ii) Scotland

40 (iii) That when two objects come into contact, material from each will leave a trace on the other

41 (iii) In a trunk in a furniture depository

42 (ii) Tyre marks

43 (i) A haberdasher's shop and a public house

44 (iii) The *Lusitania*

45 (iii) The office of the Home Secretary

46 (ii) Cumbria

47 (ii) Hypostasis

48 (ii) In a prisoner-of-war camp

49 (i) With a rifle

50 (iii) Ireland

51 (iii) Human teeth

52 (ii) Poisoned food

53 (iii) Lambeth

54 (ii) A theatre

55 (ii) The Savoy Hotel

56 (ii) In the ground under a chicken run

57 (i) Croydon, Surrey

58 (iii) In the River Thames

59 (i) A spent bullet

60 (ii) Soho

Question Rating (R3)

61 (iii) Margate, Kent

62 (ii) Her plastic dentures

63 (iii) Two open tins of paint

64 (i) London

65 (iii) An invalid chair

66 (i) In a ditch

67 (iii) On an ocean liner

68 (i) Locked in the boot of his car

69 (i) In a wood

70 (iii) Duelling pistols

71 (iii) An army camp

72 (ii) On a golf course

73 (ii) Manchester

74 (iii) Guns

75 (ii) He shot himself with his own gun

76 (iii) 'H-O-L-M-E-S'

77 (ii) She ill-treated and starved her to death

78 (i) He was an author

79 (iii) The carrier of a bicycle

80 (iii) In a sack

81 (i) A gypsy encampment

82 (ii) Braybrook Street

83 (ii) Car spray paint

84 (ii) Waterloo

85 (iii) Stoke Newington

86 (i) In a drainage ditch

87 (i) In a trunk in the hall

88 (i) On waste ground

89 (ii) Cannock Chase

90 (i) In their own dining room

Question Rating (R4)

91 (iii) In Germany

92 (i) In a shop

93 (iii) A hay fork

94 (i) In a van

95 (ii) The pattern of teeth formation from bite marks

96 (i) He stunned the victim with a blow to the head, put his head into an oven and turned on the gas

97 (i) In a hotel

98 (ii) The Savoy Hotel

99 (ii) In a fenland dyke

100 (ii) It was pushed through the porthole of a ship into the ocean

101 (ii) In a car

102 (iii) In a jeweller's shop

103 (ii) French

104 (iii) He was tied up and gagged

105 (i) Forest Gate

106 (ii) A mill

107 (iii) Epping Forest

108 (iii) In a police van

109 (ii) Southampton

110 (iii) Bradford, Yorkshire

111 (iii) A gravel pit

112 (ii) A piece of bandage made of materials used in military dressings

113 (ii) Liverpool

114 (ii) Brighton, Sussex

115 (i) A pool in the country

116 (ii) In a cemetery

117 (ii) On a ship on the high seas

118 (ii) A police station

119 (i) Floating in a river

120 (ii) Over twenty years

Question Rating (R5)

121 (i) In a disused mineshaft

122 (i) In his taxi cab

123 (iii) Leeds
124 (iii) A badge and a button
125 (iii) The King of Greece
126 (ii) A vacuum cleaner
127 (iii) A game-shooting trip
128 (i) In an unoccupied summer house
129 (ii) Because it was of a special type only issued to members of the armed forces
130 (i) In a quarry
131 (i) A raincoat and a plastic bag
132 (iii) In his basement flat
133 (iii) The Three Wise Monkeys
134 (i) In the privy
135 (iii) He was poaching rabbits
136 (iii) In her corner shop
137 (iii) It is submerged under a reservoir
138 (ii) His revolver and a pair of gloves

139 (ii) A concrete pillbox
140 (i) Englefield Green
141 (ii) Maggots of the bluebottle fly
142 (iii) A sweet shop
143 (i) A finger stall
144 (ii) Hayling Island
145 (iii) An empty blitzed shop
146 (i) In a sanatorium
147 (i) A cinema
148 (i) A block of flats
149 (iii) She was the first murderer caught as a result of distributing parts of her victim around London and the last to be burned at the stake for 'petty treason' (i.e. murdering a husband)
150 (ii) A cinema

CHAPTER NINE

ANSWERS

Question Rating (R1)

1 (ii) It is believed that it was fed to pigs on a farm

2 (i) It was the first time a murder conviction based on fingerprint evidence had been returned in a British court

3 (iii) Bambi

4 (iii) He was blown to pieces in his car by a bomb

5 (ii) Whether his behaviour is sane

6 (ii) He was American

7 (ii) Paris, France

8 (ii) Oscar Wilde

9 (ii) That she was pregnant

10 (ii) A coroner's jury

11 (i) It was the first time, in English Criminal Law, that anyone had been convicted of murder without the victim's body being found

12 (ii) In a series of arson attacks

13 (ii) Five

14 (ii) Insanity

15 (iii) By the raising of a black flag

16 (iii) Ten years of age

17 (i) From using sheep dip solution

18 (ii) They were Irish

19 (ii) Pierrepoint

20 (iii) After three unsuccessful attempts to hang him, he was reprieved

21 (ii) George Joseph Smith

22 (i) Suicide

23　(ii)　Broadmoor Hospital
24　(iii)　The Welsh Guards
25　(i)　That he was suffering from amnesia
26　(iii)　West Germany
27　(ii)　Barlinnie Prison
28　(ii)　A year and a day
29　(iii)　The Black Museum
30　(i)　Interpol

Question Rating (R2)

31　(i)　Not proven
32　(ii)　He confessed to the murder
33　(i)　It was never established
34　(ii)　He starved himself to death in prison
35　(i)　A prison
36　(iii)　A guilty man was found innocent
37　(ii)　Wandsworth Prison
38　(i)　The trial judge had misdirected the jury on the acceptability of a 'corroborated' statement by a witness
39　(ii)　He was found guilty and she not guilty
40　(ii)　'Unlawful killing'

41　(i)　Evidence of similar crimes committed by the defendant
42　(iii)　None. It is an offence at Common Law
43　(ii)　The defendant's right to remain silent
44　(iii)　The National Council for Civil Liberties
45　(i)　He was a nightclub doorman
46　(i)　He committed suicide by hanging himself
47　(ii)　Because he decided to return to Britain, of his own volition, to stand trial
48　(iii)　The common hangman
49　(i)　It was the last public execution in Britain
50　(i)　He was a butler
51　(ii)　Life imprisonment
52　(ii)　By arsenic poisoning
53　(ii)　That it was used as a cosmetic

54 (iii) There is normally no opportunity for a defendant to appeal against a conviction for an offence to which he has previously pleaded guilty

55 (i) *Rough Justice*

56 (iii) They were German

57 (ii) Eric Rothwell Holt

58 (i) That, in law, a person may not be put in peril twice for the same offence

59 (ii) He blew up a hotel

60 (iii) Paris, France

Question Rating (R3)

61 (ii) A female volunteer was immersed in a bath of water to illustrate how the victim was murdered

62 (iii) His arms

63 (ii) Australia

64 (iii) A bicycle

65 (iii) At twenty-one days it was at that time the longest murder trial of a single defendant in English legal history

66 (i) Detention at Her Majesty's pleasure

67 (i) A military court

68 (ii) Because the death penalty had been temporarily suspended in Britain

69 (iii) York

70 (iii) Broadmoor Hospital

71 (ii) He was a policeman

72 (ii) It was the first time a conviction had been set aside in a case of murder

73 (iii) 'Evidence of System'

74 (i) Cookham Wood Prison

75 (ii) He drove his motor car at her and knocked her off her bicycle

76 (iii) Bulgaria

77 (iii) He had described himself as a widower when his wife was still alive

78 (ii) The Black and Tans

79 (i) Fighting a Japanese soldier armed with a knife

80 (iii) S. A. Klosovski

81 (iii) At thirty seconds, it was the shortest British murder trial on record

82 (i) In future, the evidence of accomplices would require corroboration

83 (ii) Broadmoor Hospital

84 (ii) Because he was a citizen of the Irish Republic who committed his crime outside England

85 (iii) The power to order a new trial

86 (i) Transvestism

87 (iii) The Open University

88 (iii) Chief of the Imperial General Staff

89 (i) The British Broadcasting Corporation

90 (iii) It was the first time in a British murder trial that bloodstains were proved to have been human

Question Rating (R4)

91 (iii) James Camb

92 (iii) He was an actor

93 (ii) West Germany

94 (i) Guilty but insane

95 (iii) Evidence from hair samples

96 (i) Greed – they were in debt and wanted the victim's money

97 (i) Wandsworth Prison

98 (ii) Because of his age

99 (iii) 'The Three Musketeers'

100 (ii) He shot himself dead before he could be arrested

101 (iii) 'Murder by person or persons unknown'

102 (ii) They were both soldiers

103 (i) Because in 1931 the unsolved murder of a young woman had occurred on the Newcastle to Otterburn road – and there were similarities to Brown's crime

104 (i) Approximately 1 per cent

105 (i) She became the first woman to lead a defence in a British murder trial

106 (iii) That a medical inquiry into the sanity of anyone sentenced to death would take place

107 (iii) A duel

108 (i) Cross-examine the defendant on the whole of his past criminal record

109 (i) They wanted to sell his cadaver to an anatomist

110 (iii) He went mad and was sent to a lunatic asylum

111 (i) He was a short-story writer

112 (iii) He was a blacksmith

113 (ii) He had already been dead for three and a half years

114 (iii) It repealed the law requiring every corpse to receive a Christian burial, thus allowing bodies to be donated to medical science

115 (i) The Home Office appointed a leading QC to conduct a secret inquiry into the new evidence

116 (ii) It was thrown off a motorway bridge on to the fast lane below

117 (ii) That any member of the clergy, including those in minor orders, came under the jurisdiction of the Church and could not be punished by any temporal court

118 (i) It was the first murder prosecution to be instigated by a private individual in Britain since 1868

119 (ii) Iraq

120 (ii) That she was right handed. (An earlier damaging testimony had alleged that she used the firearm with her left hand)

Question Rating (R5)

121 (ii) French Guiana

122 (i) 'A guilty mind'

123 (i) It was the last triple execution to be carried out at that prison

124 (iii) So that the jury, at his forthcoming murder trial, would not be aware of his criminal record

125 (i) Playing with a small plastic duck

126 (iii) Prime Minister

127 (ii) Peter Louis Alphon

128 (ii) He was murdered by some of the men who had hired him in the first place

129 (iii) Madame Tussaud's

130 (i) Buckinghamshire

131 (ii) None

132 (i) She had hired a contract killer

133 (ii) He kicked her to death

134 (ii) Less than five minutes

135 (i) He fell through the trapdoor and had to grab the legs of the condemned man to save himself

136 (i) The placing of a white cap over her face

137 (iii) He cut her throat

138 (i) He was the first man to hang in Armley Gaol's newly constructed execution shed

139 (iii) An anonymous letter, naming Turner, was sent to the police by a family friend

140 (ii) Stop every vehicle, on main roads, driving from London to the south coast

141 (iii) Fanny Adams

142 (iii) He was on parole from prison

143 (i) A novel, written by him, about the capture, torture and death of a boy

144 (ii) It was the capital's largest multiple execution in over a century

145 (i) She had been bludgeoned to death with a hammer

146 (iii) The victim's skull

147 (i) The last nobleman in England to suffer a felon's death

148 (ii) He carried P.C. Meehan along the road clinging to his vehicle, until he was thrown from it and went under an oncoming car

149 (ii) At ninety-two days it was the longest stay ever recorded in a British murder case. He was then reprieved

150 (ii) He tried to gouge out his eyes

SELF-RATING CHART

	Total points available for each chapter 450				Total points available for whole quiz 4,050

Points scored per chapter	Rating	Points scored for whole quiz
380 or over	SUPER SLEUTH	3,450 or over
315 or over	EXCELLENT	2,800 or over
250 or over	VERY GOOD	2,230 or over
180 or over	GOOD	1,625 or over
112 or over	FAIR	1,000 or over
65 or over	SOME KNOWLEDGE	600 or over
25 or over	LITTLE KNOWLEDGE	200 or over
0 or over	UNRATED	0 or over

BIBLIOGRAPHY

John Askill and Martyn Sharpe, *Angel of Death*, Michael O'Mara Books Ltd, 1993

James Bland, *True Crime Diary*, Futura Publications, 1987

——, *True Crime Diary Volume 2*, Futura Publications, 1989

Fenton Bresler, *An Almanac of Murder*, Severn House Publishers Ltd, 1987

Robert Church, *More Murder in East Anglia*, Robert Hale Ltd, 1990

Martin Fido, *Murder Guide to London*, George Weidenfeld and Nicolson Ltd, 1986

J. H. H. Gaute and Robin Odell, *The New Murderers' Who's Who*, Headline Book Publishing PLC, 1989

——, *Murder Whodunnit?*, Pan Books Ltd, 1984

——, *Murder Whereabouts*, Harrap Ltd, 1986

Jonathan Goodman (Ed.), *The Art of Murder*, Judy Piatkus (Publishers) Ltd, 1990

——, *The Christmas Murders*, Sphere Books Ltd, 1988

——, *The Seaside Murders*, Sphere Books Ltd, 1985

Leo Grex, *These Crimes Made Headlines*, Robert Hale Ltd, 1980

Gordon Honeycombe, *The Murders of the Black Museum 1870–1970*, (Special revised edition), Arrow Books, 1984

John Janaway, *Surrey Murders*, Countryside Books, 1988

Brian Lane, *The Encyclopaedia of Forensic Science*, Headline Book Publishing PLC, 1992

——, *The Murder Club*, Harrap Ltd, 1989

——, *The Murder Guide*, Robinson Publishing, 1991

T. J. Leech, *A Date with the Hangman*, Forum Press Book (an imprint of True Crime Library No. 3), 1992

Roy Harley Lewis, *Edwardian Murders*, David and Charles Publishers PLC, 1989

Georgina Lloyd, *The Evil that Men Do*, Bantam Books, 1992

——, *Murders Unspeakable*, Robert Hale Ltd, 1992

——, *One Was Not Enough*, Bantam Books, 1992

——, *With Malice Aforethought*, Bantam Books, 1990

Brian Marriner, *A Century of Sex Killers*, True Crime Library No. 1, A Forum Press Book, 1992

Professor Keith Simpson, *Forty Years of Murder*, Grafton, 1980

Frank Smyth, *Cause of Death*, Pan Books Ltd, 1982

Richard and Molly Whittington-Egan, *The Bedside Book of Murder*, David and Charles Publications PLC, 1988

George Theodore Wilkinson, *The Newgate Calendar*, Sphere Books Ltd, 1991

Colin Wilson, *The Mammoth Book of True Crime* (Volume 1), Robinson Publishing, 1988

Colin Wilson and Patricia Pitman, *Encyclopaedia of Murder*, Pan Books Ltd, 1964

——, *Encyclopaedia of Modern Murder 1962–1982*, Arthur Barker Ltd, 1983

Colin Wilson and Donald Seaman, *The Serial Killers*, True Crime, 1992

Infamous Crimes that Shocked the World, Macdonald and Company Publishers Ltd, 1989 (reprinted under the Black Cat imprint)